BIOZONE

Biology ... k

Health & Disease

BIOZONE's writing team

Tracey Greenwood

Lissa Bainbridge-Smith

Richard Allan

Artwork by Daniel Butler

First Edition 2006
Second edition 2007
Third printing

ISBN: 978-1-877462-13-9

Copyright ©2007 **BIOZONE International Ltd**
Published by: **BIOZONE International Ltd**

Printed by BR Printers

Distribution Offices:
Head office (New Zealand)
Biozone International Ltd, NZ

Telephone: 07-856-8104
Fax: 07-856-9243
Email: sales@biozone.co.nz
Website: www.biozone.co.nz

United Kingdom & Europe
Biozone Learning Media (UK) Ltd, UK
Telephone: +44 (0)1746 250006
Email: sales@biozone.co.uk
Website: www.biozone.co.uk

Australia
Biozone Learning Media Australia, Australia
Telephone: 07-5535-4896
Fax: 07-5508-2432
Email: sales@biozone.com.au
Website: www.biozone.com.au

USA
Biozone Corporation
FREE phone: 855-246-4555
FREE fax: 855-935-3555
Email: sales@thebiozone.com
Website: www.thebiozone.com

Front cover photographs:
Stethoscopes. Image ©2005 JupiterImages Corporation www.clipart.com

Patient examination. Image ©1996 Digital Stock Corporation (Medicine & Healthcare collection)

Meet the writing team

Tracey Greenwood
I have been writing resources for students since 1993. I have a Ph.D in biology, specialising in lake ecology and I have taught both graduate and undergraduate biology.

Tracey
Senior Author

Lissa Bainbridge-Smith
I worked in industry in a research and development capacity for eight years before joining BIOZONE in 2006. I have an M.Sc from Waikato University.

Lissa
Author

Kent Pryor
I have a BSc from Massey University majoring in zoology and ecology and taught secondary school biology and chemistry for 9 years before joining BIOZONE as an author in 2009.

Kent
Author

Richard Allan
I have had 11 years experience teaching senior secondary school biology. I have a Masters degree in biology and founded BIOZONE in the 1980s after developing resources for my own students.

Richard
Founder & CEO

Biology Modular Workbook Series

The Biozone *Biology Modular Workbook Series* has been developed to meet the demands of customers with the requirement for a modular resource which can be used in a flexible way. Like Biozone's popular Student Resource and Activity Manuals, these workbooks provide a collection of visually interesting and accessible activities, which cater for students with a wide range of abilities and background. The workbooks are divided into a series of chapters, each comprising an introductory section with detailed learning objectives and useful resources, and a series of write-on activities ranging from paper practicals and data handling exercises, to questions requiring short essay style answers. A new feature in this edition is the inclusion of page tabs identifying "**Related activities**" in the workbook. These will help students to locate related material for help or additional detail if it is required. Material for these workbooks has been drawn from Biozone's popular, widely used manuals, but the workbooks have been structured with greater ease of use and flexibility in mind. During the development of this series, we have taken the opportunity to improve the design and content, while retaining the basic philosophy of a student-friendly resource which spans the gulf between textbook and study guide. With its unique, highly visual presentation, it is possible to engage and challenge students, increase their motivation and empower them to take control of their learning.

Health & Disease

This title in the *Biology Modular Workbook Series* provides students with a set of comprehensive guidelines and highly visual worksheets through which to explore aspects of human health and disease and the role of modern medicine in treating and preventing health disorders. *Health & Disease* is the ideal companion for students of the life sciences, encompassing not only infectious and non-infectious disease, but the nature of immunity, immune system dysfunction, preventative and diagnostic techniques, and treatments for disease. This workbook comprises four chapters, each covering a different aspect of human health. These areas are explained through a series of one and two page activities, each of which explores a specific concept (e.g. cancer or malaria). Model answers (on CD-ROM) accompany each order free of charge. *Health & Disease* is a student-centred resource. Students completing the activities, in concert with their other classroom and practical work, will consolidate existing knowledge and develop and practise skills that they will use throughout their course. This workbook may be used in the classroom or at home as a supplement to a standard textbook. Some activities are introductory in nature, while others may be used to consolidate and test concepts already covered by other means. Biozone has a commitment to produce a cost-effective, high quality resource, which acts as a student's companion throughout their biology study. Please do not photocopy from this workbook; we cannot afford to provide single copies of workbooks to schools and continue to develop, update, and improve the material they contain.

Acknowledgements and Photo Credits

• Joan and John Allan for kindly agreeing to pose for the photos on age related health issues • Joseph E. Armstrong, Professor of Botany, Head Curator at ISU Herbarium, USA for his permission to use the photo showing a child with kwashiorkor • Bio-Rad Laboratories, Inc. for allowing us to photograph the Helios gene gun• Hemosol Inc. for use of their photograph in the blood substitutes activity • Sue Fitzgerald and Mary McDougall for their efficient handling of the office • Dr. Nita Scobie, Cytogenetics Department, Waikato Hospital for chromosome photos • Genesis Research and Development Corp. Auckland, for the photo used on the HGP activity • ©1999 University of Kansas, for the photo of the incubator for culture of cell lines • Charles Goldberg, University of California, San Diego School of Medicine, for the photograph of a patient with rheumatoid arthritis • Totem Graphics, for their clipart collection of plants and animals • TechPool Studios, for their fabulous clipart collection of human anatomy: Copyright ©1994, TechPool Studios Corp. USA (some images were modified by R. Allan and T. Greenwood) • Corel Corporation, for clipart of plants and animals from the Corel MEGAGALLERY collection • 3D models created using Poser IV, Curious Labs. Photos kindly provided by individuals or corporations have been indentified by way of coded credits as follows: **CDC**: Centers for Disease Control and Prevention, Atlanta, USA, **EII**: Education Interactive Imaging, **Eyewire**: Eyewire Inc © 1998-2001, www.eyewire.com, **HGSI**: Dena Borchardt at Human Genome Sciences Inc., **NICD**: National Institute on Chemical Dependency, **RA**: Richard Allan

Also in this series:

Skills in Biology

Genes & Inheritance

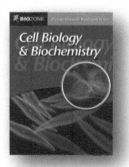

Microbiology & Biotechnology

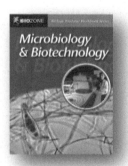

Cell Biology & Biochemistry

For other titles in this series go to:
www.thebiozone.com/modular.html

How to Use this Workbook

Health & Disease is designed to provide students with a resource that will make the acquisition of knowledge and skills in this area easier and more enjoyable. The study of disease, its role in human societies, and its prevention and treatment are important in many biology curricula. Moreover, this subject is of high interest, being topical, rapidly changing, and highly relevant to students in their everyday life. This workbook is suitable for all students of the life sciences, and will reinforce and extend the ideas developed by teachers. It is **not a textbook**; its aim is to complement the texts written for your particular course. *Health & Disease* provides the following resources in each chapter. You should refer back to them as you work through each set of worksheets.

Activity Pages

The activities and exercises make up most of the content of this workbook. They are designed to reinforce the concepts you have learned about in the topic. Your teacher may use the activity pages to introduce a topic for the first time, or you may use them to revise ideas already covered. They are excellent for use in the classroom, and as homework exercises and revision. In most cases, the activities should not be attempted until you have carried out the necessary background reading from your textbook. As a self-check, model answers for each activity are provided on CD-ROM with each order of workbooks.

Resources Information

Your set textbook should always be a starting point for information, but there are also many other resources available. A list of readily available resources is provided below. Please note that our listing of any product in this workbook does not denote Biozone's endorsement of it.

Supplementary Texts

Chenn, P., 1997.
Microorganisms and Biotechnology, 176 pp.
ISBN: 0-71957-509-5
Good coverage of the nature of microorganisms, their culture and growth, and their roles in biotechnology. It includes chapters on the genetic engineering of microbes and enzyme technology.

Clegg, C.J., 2002.
Microbes in Action, 92 pp.
ISBN: 0-71957-554-0
Microbes and their roles in disease and biotechnology. It includes material on the diversity of the microbial world, microbiological techniques, and a short account of enzyme technology.

Freeland, P., 1999
Hodder Advanced Science: Microbes, Medicine, and Commerce, 160 pp.
Publisher: Hodder and Stoughton
ISBN: 0340731036
Comments: *Coverage of biotechnology, microbiology, pathology, and immunity.*

Fullick, A., 1998
Human Health and Disease, 162 pp.
Publisher: Heinemann Educational Publishers
ISBN: 0435570919
Comments: *An excellent supplement for courses with modules in human health and disease. Includes infectious and non-infectious disease.*

Hudson, T. and K. Mannion, 2001.
Microbes and Disease, 104 pp.
ISBN: 0-00-327742-9
Coverage of selected aspects of microbiology including the culture and applications of bacteria, and the role of bacteria and viruses in disease. Immunity, vaccination, and antimicrobial drug use are covered in the concluding chapter.

Murray, P. & N. Owens, 2001.
Behaviour and Populations, 82 pp.
ISBN: 0-00-327743-7
This text covers an eclectic range of topics including patterns of behaviour, reproduction and its control, human growth and development, human populations, aspects of infectious disease, and issues related to health and lifestyle.

Taylor, J., 2001.
Microorganisms and Biotechnology, 192 pp.
Publisher: NelsonThornes. Available in Australia through Thomson Learning
ISBN: 0-17-448255-8
Comments: *Good coverage of this topic, including pathogens and disease, defence, and the use of microbes in industry and medicine.*

Biology Dictionaries

Access to a good biology dictionary is useful when dealing with biological terms. Some of the titles available are listed below. Link to the relevant publisher via Biozone's resources hub.

Clamp, A. **AS/A-Level Biology. Essential Word Dictionary**, 2000, 161 pp. Philip Allan Updates. **ISBN**: 0-86003-372-4.
Carefully selected essential words for AS and A2. Concise definitions are supported by further explanation and illustrations where required.

Hale, W.G. **Collins: Dictionary of Biology** 4 ed. 2005, 528 pp. Collins.
ISBN: 0-00-720734-4.
Updated to take in the latest developments in biology and now internet-linked. The earlier edition, ISBN: 0-00-714709-0, is also still available though amazon. com in North America).

Henderson, I.F, W.D. Henderson, and E. Lawrence. **Henderson's Dictionary of Biological Terms**, 1999, 736 pp. Prentice Hall. **ISBN**: 0582414989
This edition has been updated, rewritten for clarity, and reorganised for ease of use. An essential reference and the dictionary of choice for many.

McGraw-Hill (ed). **McGraw-Hill Dictionary of Bioscience**, 2 ed., 2002, 662 pp. McGraw-Hill.
ISBN: 0-07-141043-0
22 000 entries encompassing more than 20 areas of the life sciences. It includes synonyms, acronyms, abbreviations, and pronunciations for all terms.

Periodicals, Magazines, & Journals

Biological Sciences Review: *An informative quarterly publication for biology students. Enquiries: Philip Allan Publishers, Market Place, Deddington, Oxfordshire OX 15 OSE* **Tel**: 01869 338652 **Fax**: 01869 338803 **E-mail**: sales@philipallan.co.uk *or subscribe from their web site.*

New Scientist: *Widely available weekly magazine with research summaries and features. Enquiries: Reed Business Information Ltd, 51 Wardour St. London WIV 4BN* **Tel**: (UK and intl):+44 (0) 1444 475636 **E-mail**: ns.subs@qss-uk.com *or subscribe from their web site.*

Scientific American: *A monthly magazine containing specialist features. Articles range in level of reading difficulty and assumed knowledge. Subscription enquiries: 415 Madison Ave. New York. NY10017-1111* **Tel**: (outside North America): 515-247-7631 **Tel**: (US& Canada): 800-333-1199

School Science Review: *A quarterly journal which includes articles, reviews, and news on current research and curriculum development. Free to Ordinary Members of the ASE or available on subscription. Enquiries:* **Tel**: 01707 28300 **Email**: info@ase.org.uk *or visit their web site.*

The American Biology Teacher: *The peer-reviewed journal of the NABT. Published nine times a year and containing information and activities relevant to biology teachers.* Contact: NABT, 12030 Sunrise Valley Drive, #110, Reston, VA 20191-3409 **Web**: www.nabt.org

Defence and the Immune System

Defence mechanisms against disease: immune system function and dysfunction

Recognising self and non-self. Non-specific and specific defence mechanisms. Cell-mediated and humoral immunity. Autoimmunity.

Learning Objectives

☐ 1. Compile your own glossary from the **KEY WORDS** displayed in **bold type** in the learning objectives below.

Recognising Self and Non-self *(pages 10-11)*

☐ 2. Explain how a body is able to distinguish between self and non-self and comment on the importance of this.

☐ 3. Explain the nature of **major histocompatibility complex (MHC)** (including the HLA antigens) and its role in **self-recognition** and in determining tissue compatibility in transplant recipients.

☐ 4. Explain the basis of the **Rh** and **ABO blood group systems** in humans. Explain the consequences of blood type incompatibility in blood transfusions.

☐ 5. Discuss how **self-recognition** poses problems for tissue and organ transplants. Determine the physiological basis of transplant rejection and suggest how it may be avoided. Explain why it is so difficult to find compatible tissue and organ donors. Suggest how this problem might be solved in the future.

Defence Mechanisms

Non-specific defences *(pages 12-17, 25-26)*

☐ 6. Explain what is meant by a **non-specific defence mechanism**. Distinguish between first and second lines of defence. Describe the nature and role of each of the following in protecting against pathogens:

   Preventing pathogen entry (the first line of defence)
   (a) Skin (including sweat and sebum production).
   (b) Mucus-secreting and ciliated membranes.
   (c) Body secretions (tears, urine, saliva, gastric juice).
   (d) Blood clotting and the role of platelets.

   Non-specific defence after pathogen entry (the second line of defence)
   (e) Natural anti-bacterial and anti-viral proteins such as **interferon** and **complement**.
   (f) The **inflammatory response, fever**, and cell death.
   (g) **Phagocytosis** by phagocytes. Recognise the term phagocyte as referring to any of a number of phagocytic leucocytes (e.g. macrophages).
   (h) Know that leucocytes (including those also involved in specific defences) are present in the body at different proportions, and that a change in proportions may indicate the presence of a disease or infection.

Specific defences *(pages 18, 23, 25-26)*

☐ 7. Identify the **third line of defence** (specific resistance). Contrast specific and non-specific defences in terms of time for activation and **specificity** towards a pathogen.

☐ 8. Briefly explain what is meant by an **immune response**. Appreciate how the immune response involves recognition of, and response to, foreign material.

☐ 9. Explain the importance of retaining the memory of a foreign body and being able to respond to it in the future. Describe what is meant by the immune system having both **specificity** and **memory**. Providing examples, distinguish between **naturally acquired** and **artificially acquired immunity** and between **active** and **passive immunity**. Compare the duration of the immunity gained by active and passive means. Define: vaccine and immunisation.

☐ 10. Recognise the role of the **lymphatic system** in the production and transport of leucocytes.

The Immune System *(pages 18-22, 101-107)*

☐ 11. Distinguish between: **cell-mediated immunity** and **humoral (antibody-mediated) immunity**.

☐ 12. Explain the role of **lymphocytes** in the immune response. With respect to structure and function, distinguish between the two kinds of lymphocyte: **B cells** and **T cells**, and explain the origin of each type.

☐ 13. Recall that other types of white blood cells are involved in non-specific defence mechanisms.

☐ 14. Recognise the contribution to immunology of **Sir Frank McFarlane Burnet** through the development of the **clonal selection theory** (see #15-16 below).

☐ 15. Outline the theory of **clonal selection** and the basis of **immunological memory**. Explain how the immune system is able to respond to the large, unpredictable range of potential antigens in the environment.

☐ 16. Appreciate that self-tolerance occurs during development as a result of the selective destruction of the B cells that react to self-antigens.

☐ 17. Explain the role of the **thymus** in the immune response. Describe the nature, origin, and role of **macrophages** (a type of phagocyte). Appreciate the role of macrophages in processing and presenting foreign antigens and in stimulating lymphocyte activity.

Cell-mediated immunity

☐ 18. Describe the various roles of T lymphocytes in **cell-mediated immunity**. Describe how T cells recognise specific foreign antigens.

☐ 19. If required, describe the functional roles of the different named T cells, including the **cytotoxic** (killer) **T cells** (T_C) and the **helper T cells** (T_H). Identify the organisms/cells against which these T cells act.

☐ 20. Appreciate the role of T lymphocytes in the rejection of transplanted tissues and organs.

Humoral immunity

☐ 21. Define the terms: **antibody**, **antigen**, **immunoglobulin**. Name some common antigens and explain their role in provoking a specific immune response.

☐ 22. Describe the structure of an antibody identifying the constant and variable regions, and the **antigen binding site**. Relate antibody structure to function.

☐ 23. Explain antibody production, including how B cells bring about **humoral** (antibody-mediated) **immunity** to specific antigens. If required, provide an explanation of how antigens are presented, the role of **helper T cells**, and the activation and differentiation of B-cells.

☐ 24. Describe and contrast the functional roles of **plasma cells** and **memory cells** and recall the basis for immunological memory. Appreciate the role of immunological memory in long term immunity (ability to respond quickly to previously encountered antigens).

☐ 25. Describe the methods by which antibodies inactivate antigens and facilitate their destruction.

☐ 26. Describe what is meant by a **primary** and a **secondary response** to infection. Explain the role of these responses, as well as immune system memory, in the success of **vaccines** against specific pathogens (cross reference with the objectives and activities in the topic *Preventing and Treating Disease*).

☐ 27. Explain the principles behind the production of **monoclonal antibodies**. Describe their role of in diagnosiing and treating disease (cross reference with the topic *Preventing and Treating Disease*).

Hypersensitivity Reactions *(pages 24, 27)*

☐ 28. Explain what is meant by an **autoimmune disease** and provide examples. Recognise an allergic response as an inappropriate immune response to an **allergen**. Identify some of the common triggers for allergies in susceptible people.

☐ 29. With reference to **asthma** or **hayfever**, outline the role of the immune system in allergic reactions, including the role of **histamine** in these allergies.

See page 7 for additional details of this text:

■ Chenn, P. 1997. **Microorganisms and Biotechnology** (John Murray), chpt. 9 as required.

■ Freeland, P., 1999. **Microbes, Medicine and Commerce** (Hodder & Stoughton), chpt 6.

■ Fullick, A., 1998. **Human Health and Disease** (Heinemann), chpt. 2-3.

■ Hudson, T. & K. Mannion, 2001. **Microbes and Disease** (Collins), chpt. 6.

■ Taylor, J., 2001. **Microorganisms and Biotechnology** (NelsonThornes), chpt. 7.

See page 7 for details of publishers of periodicals:

STUDENT'S REFERENCE

Self-recognition & the immune system

■ **Skin, Scabs and Scars** Biol. Sci. Rev., 17(3) Feb. 2005, pp. 2-6. *The many roles of skin, including its importance in wound healing and the processes involved in its repair when damaged.*

■ **Inflammation** Biol. Sci. Rev., 17(1) Sept. 2004, pp. 18-20. *The role of this nonspecific defense response to tissue injury and infection. The processes involved in inflammation are discussed.*

■ **The Skin** Australasian Science 17(4), Summer 1996, pp. 9-12. *The skin as the body's largest organ has an important role in providing a physical and active barrier to the invasion of pathogens.*

■ **Antibodies** Biol. Sci. Rev., 11(3) January 1999, pp. 34-35. *The operation of the immune system and the production of antibodies (including procedures for producing monoclonal antibodies).*

■ **Lymphocytes - The Heart of the Immune System** Biol. Sci. Rev., 12 (1) September 1999 pp. 32-35. *An excellent account of the role of lymphocytes in the immune response (includes the types and actions of different lymphocytes).*

■ **Red Blood Cells** Biol. Sci. Rev., 11(2) November 1998, pp. 2-4. *The function of red blood cells, including their role in antigenic recognition.*

■ **Monoclonals as Medicines** Biol. Sci. Rev., 18(4) April 2006, pp. 38-40. *The use of monoclonal antibodies in therapeutic and diagnostic medicine.*

■ **Beware! Allergens** New Scientist, 22 January 2000 (Inside Science). *The allergic response: sensitisation and the role of the immune system.*

■ **Anaphylactic Shock.** Biol. Sci. Rev., 19(2) Nov. 2006, pp. 11-13. *An account of anaphylactic shock, a sever allergic reaction caused by a massive overreaction of the body's immune system.*

■ **Blood Group Antigens** Biol. Sci. Rev., 9(5) May 1997, pp. 10-13. *An excellent short account of the ABO and rhesus system in humans.*

■ **Fanning the Flames** New Scientist, 22 May 2004, pp. 40-43. *Inflammation is one of the first lines of internal defence, but it has been implicated in a host of disparate diseases.*

■ **Misery for all Seasons** National Geographic, 209(5) May 2006, pp. 116-135. *The causes, effects, and prevention of common allergies.*

TEACHER'S REFERENCE

Self-recognition & the immune system

■ **Inside Trading** New Scientist, 26 June 1999, pp. 42-46. *How do we maintain a stable relationship with our microflora and protect ourselves from attack by pathogens?*

■ **Life, Death, and the Immune System** Scientific American, Sept. 1993. *An entire special issue on human infection, immune system, and disease.*

■ **Let Them Eat Dirt** New Scientist, 18 July 1998, pp. 26-31. *Effective, normal immune system function may require a certain level of early exposure to bacteria and other microorganisms..*

■ **The Long Arm of the Immune System** Sci. American, Nov. 2002, pp. 34-41. *The role of dendritic cells, a class of leucocytes with a role in activating the immune system (good extension).*

■ **How Interferons Fight Disease** Scientific American, May 1994, pp. 40-47. *The interferons of the human immune system and their active role in immune system function. Interferons can even activate immune system cells to attack tumors.*

■ **Immunotherapy** Biol. Sci. Rev., 15(1), Sept. 2002, pp. 39-41. *Medical research is uncovering ways in which our immune system can be used in developing vaccines for cancer.*

Hypersensitivity and immune failure

■ **Taming Lupus** Scientific American, March 2005, pp. 58-65. *An account of the autoimmune disorder, lupus: its causes, pathways to disease, triggers for disease onset, and possible treatments.*

■ **Filthy Friends** New Scientist,16 April 2005, pp. 34-39. *Early contact with a range of harmless microbes may be important in reducing the risk of hypersensitivity reactions.*

■ **Peacekeepers of the Immune System** Scientific American, Oct. 2006, pp. 34-41. *Regulatory T cells suppress immune activity and combat autoimmunity.*

See pages 4-5 for details of how to access **Bio Links** from our web site: **www.thebiozone.com** From Bio Links, access sites under the topics:

GENERAL BIOLOGY ONLINE RESOURCES > Online Textbooks and Lecture Notes: • S-Cool! A level biology revision guide • Kimball's biology pages Learn.co.uk • Mr Biology's biology web site • Welcome to the biology web... *and others* > **General online biology resources:** • AP interactive animation • Acccess excellence • How stuff works • Ken's bioweb resources • National Association of Biology Teachers • Virtual library: Biosciences > **Glossaries:** • Animal anatomy glossary • Kimball's biology glossary

ANIMAL BIOLOGY: • Anatomy and physiology • Human physiology lecture notes ... *and others*

HEALTH & DISEASE > Defence and the Immune System: • Blood group antigens • Inducible defences against pathogens • National Institute of Allergy and infectious Disease • Microbiology and immunology • Primary immunodeficiency diseases • The immune system: An overview • Understanding the immune system • Tissue defences against pathogens • Welcome to the National Blood Service ... *and others*

Presentation MEDIA to support this topic:

HEALTH & DISEASE:
• Defence and Immunity

Targets for Defence

In order for the body to present an effective defence against pathogens, it must first be able to recognise its own tissues (self). It must also ignore the normal microflora inhabiting our bodies and be able to deal with abnormal cells which periodically appear in the body and might develop into cancer. Failure of self/non-self recognition can lead to autoimmune disorders, in which the immune system mistakenly destroys its own tissues. The ability of the body to recognise its own molecules has implications for medical techniques such as tissue grafts, organ transplants, and blood transfusions. Incompatible tissues (correctly identified as foreign) are attacked by the body's immune system (rejection). Even a healthy pregnancy involves suppression of specific features of the self recognition system, allowing the mother to tolerate a nine month relationship with a foreign body (a fetus).

The Body's Natural Microbiota

After birth, normal and characteristic microbial populations begin to establish themselves on and in the body. A typical human body contains 1×10^{13} body cells, yet harbors 1×10^{14} bacterial cells. These microorganisms establish more or less permanent residence but, under normal conditions, do not cause disease. In fact, this normal microflora can benefit the host by preventing the overgrowth of harmful pathogens. They are not found throughout the entire body, but are located in certain regions.

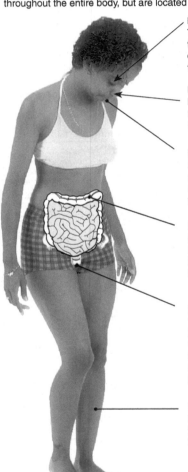

Eyes
The conjuctiva, a continuation of the skin or mucous membrane, contains a similar microbiota to the skin.

Nose and throat
Harbors a variety of microorganisms, e.g. *Staphylococcus* spp.

Mouth
Supports a large and diverse microbiota. It is an ideal microbial environment; high in moisture, warmth, and nutrient availability.

Large intestine
Contains the body's largest resident population of microbes because of its available moisture and nutrients.

Urinary and genital systems
The lower urethra in both sexes has a resident population; the vagina has a particular acid-tolerant population of microbes because of the low pH nature of its secretions.

Skin
Skin secretions prevent most of the microbes on the skin from becoming residents.

The Major Histocompatibility Complex

The human immune system achieves self-recognition through the **major histocompatibility complex** (MHC). This is a cluster of tightly linked genes on chromosome 6 in humans. These genes code for protein molecules called MHC antigens (also called HLA antigens for human leukocyte antigens) which are attached to the surface of body cells. They are used by the immune system to recognize its own or foreign material. **Class I MHC** antigens are located on the surface of virtually all human cells, but **Class II MHC** antigens are restricted to macrophages and the antibody-producing B-lymphocytes.

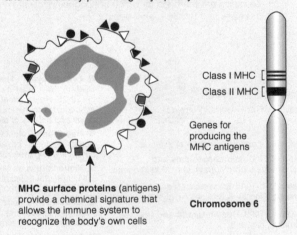

Class I MHC [
Class II MHC [

Genes for producing the MHC antigens

Chromosome 6

MHC surface proteins (antigens) provide a chemical signature that allows the immune system to recognize the body's own cells

Tissue Transplants

The MHC is responsible for the rejection of tissue grafts and organ transplants. Foreign MHC molecules are antigenic, causing the immune system to respond in the following way:

▸ T cells directly lyse the foreign cells

▸ Macrophages are activated by T cells and engulf foreign cells

▸ Antibodies are released that attack the foreign cell

▸ The complement system injures blood vessels supplying the graft or transplanted organ

To minimize this rejection, attempts are made to match the MHC of the donor to that of the recipient as closely as possible.

1. Explain why it is healthy to have a natural population of microbes on and inside the body: _____

_____

2. (a) Explain the nature and purpose of the major histocompatibility complex (MHC): _____

_____

_____

_____

(b) Explain the importance of such a self-recognition system: _____

_____

3. Name two situations when the body's recognition of 'self' is undesirable: _____

© BIOZONE International 2007
ISBN: 978-1-877462-13-9
Photocopying Prohibited

Related activities: The Body's Defences

Blood Group Antigens

Blood groups classify blood according to the different marker proteins on the surface of red blood cells (RBCs). These marker proteins act as **antigens** and affect the ability of RBCs to provoke an immune response. The **ABO blood group** is the most important blood typing system in medical practice, because of the presence of anti-A and anti-B antibodies in nearly all people who lack the corresponding red cell antigens (these antibodies are carried in the plasma and are present at birth). If a patient is to receive blood from a blood donor, that blood must be compatible otherwise the red blood cells of the donated blood will clump together (agglutinate), break apart, and block capillaries. There is a small margin of safety in certain blood group combinations, because the volume of donated blood is usually relatively small and the donor's antibodies are quickly diluted in the plasma. In practice, blood is carefully matched, not only for ABO types, but for other types as well. Although human RBCs have more than 500 known antigens, fewer than 30 (in 9 blood groups) are regularly tested for when blood is donated for transfusion. The blood groups involved are: *ABO, Rh, MNS, P, Lewis, Lutheran, Kell, Duffy,* and *Kidd.* The ABO and rhesus (Rh) are the best known. Although blood typing has important applications in medicine, it can also be used to rule out individuals in cases of crime (or paternity) and establish a list of potential suspects (or fathers).

1. Complete the table above to show the antibodies and antigens in each blood group, and donor/recipient blood types:

2. In a hypothetical murder case, blood from both the victim and the murderer was left at the scene. There were five suspects under investigation:

   (a) Describe what blood typing could establish about the guilt or innocence of the suspects: _____

   _____

   (b) Identify what a blood typing could not establish: _____

   _____

   (c) Suggest how the murderer's identity could be firmly established (assuming that s/he was one of the five suspects):

   _____

   (d) Explain why blood typing is not used forensically to any great extent: _____

   _____

3. Explain why the discovery of the ABO system was such a significant medical breakthrough: _____

   _____

Blood Clotting and Defence

Apart from its transport role, **blood** has a role in the body's defence against infection and **haemostasis** (the prevention of bleeding and maintenance of blood volume). The tearing or puncturing of a blood vessel initiates **clotting**. Clotting is normally a rapid process that seals off the tear, preventing blood loss and the invasion of bacteria into the site. Clot formation is triggered by the release of clotting factors from the damaged cells at the site of the tear or puncture. A hardened clot forms a scab, which acts to prevent further blood loss and acts as a mechanical barrier to the entry of pathogens.

1. Explain two roles of the blood clotting system in internal defence and haemostasis:

    (a) _____

    (b) _____

2. Explain the role of each of the following in the sequence of events leading to a blood clot:

    (a) Injury: _____

    (b) Release of chemicals from platelets: _____

    _____

    (c) Clumping of platelets at the wound site: _____

    _____

    (d) Formation of a fibrin clot: _____

    _____

3. (a) Explain the role of clotting factors in the blood in formation of the clot: _____

    _____

    (b) Explain why these clotting factors are not normally present in the plasma: _____

    _____

4. (a) Name one inherited disease caused by the absence of a clotting factor: _____

    (b) Name the clotting factor involved: _____

© BIOZONE International 2007
ISBN: 978-1-877462-13-9
Photocopying Prohibited

The Body's Defences

If microorganisms never encountered resistance from our body defences, we would be constantly ill and would eventually die of various diseases. Fortunately, in most cases our defences prevent this from happening. Some of these defences are designed to keep microorganisms from entering the body. Other defences remove the microorganisms if they manage to get inside. Further defences attack the microorganisms if they remain inside the body. The ability to ward off disease through the various defence mechanisms is called **resistance**. The lack of resistance, or vulnerability to disease, is known as **susceptibility**. One form of defence is referred to as **non-specific resistance**, and includes defences that protect us from any pathogen. This includes a first line of defence such as the physical barriers to infection (skin and mucous membranes) and a second line of defence (phagocytes, inflammation, fever, and antimicrobial substances). **Specific resistance** is a third line of defence that forms the **immune response** and targets specific pathogens. Specialised cells of the immune system, called lymphocytes, produce specific proteins called antibodies which are produced against specific antigens.

Defence & the Immune System

1. Compare and contrast the type of response against pathogens carried out by each of the three levels of defence:

_____

_____

_____

_____

_____

_____

_____

_____

_____

_____

Related activities: Targets for Defence, The Action of Phagocytes, Inflammation, Fever, The Immune System

RA 2

2. Distinguish between specific and non-specific resistance: _____

_____

_____

_____

_____

3. Discuss the features of the different types of white blood cells, explaining how these relate to their role in defence:

_____

_____

_____

_____

_____

_____

_____

_____

_____

_____

4. Describe the functional role of each of the following defence mechanisms (the first one has been completed for you):

   (a) Skin (including sweat and sebum production): _Skin helps to prevent direct entry of pathogens_
       into the body. Sebum slows growth of bacteria and fungi.

   (b) Phagocytosis by white blood cells: _____

       _____

   (c) Mucus-secreting and ciliated membranes: _____

       _____

   (d) Body secretions: tears, urine, saliva, gastric juice: _____

       _____

   (e) Natural antimicrobial proteins (e.g. interferon): _____

       _____

   (f) Antibody production: _____

       _____

   (g) Fever: _____

       _____

   (h) Cell-mediated immunity: _____

       _____

   (i) The inflammatory response: _____

       _____

5. Infection with HIV results in the progressive destruction of T lymphocytes. Suggest why this leads to an increasing number of opportunistic infections in AIDS sufferers:

_____

_____

© BIOZONE International 2007
ISBN: 978-1-877462-13-9
Photocopying Prohibited

The Action of Phagocytes

Human cells that ingest microbes and digest them by the process of **phagocytosis** are called **phagocytes**. All are types of white blood cells. During many kinds of infections, especially bacterial infections, the total number of white blood cells increases by two to four times the normal number. The ratio of various white blood cell types changes during the course of an infection.

1. Identify the white blood cells capable of phagocytosis: _____

   _____

2. Describe how a blood sample from a patient may be used to determine whether they have a microbial infection (without looking for the microbes themselves):

   _____

   _____

3. Explain how some microbes are able to overcome phagocytic cells and use them to their advantage:

   _____

   _____

Related activities: The Body's Defences

A 2

Inflammation

Damage to the body's tissues can be caused by physical agents (e.g. sharp objects, heat, radiant energy, or electricity), microbial infection, or chemical agents (e.g. gases, acids and bases). The damage triggers a defensive response called **inflammation**. It is usually characterised by four symptoms: pain, redness, heat and swelling. The inflammatory response is beneficial and has the following functions: (1) to destroy the cause of the infection and remove it and its products from the body; (2) if this fails, to limit the effects on the body by confining the infection to a small area; (3) replacing or repairing tissue damaged by the infection. The process of inflammation can be divided into three distinct stages. These are described below.

1. Outline the three **stages** of inflammation and identify the beneficial role of each stage:

    (a) _____

    _____

    (b) _____

    _____

    (c) _____

    _____

2. Identify two features of phagocytes important in the response to microbial invasion: _____

    _____

3. State the role of histamines and prostaglandins in inflammation: _____

4. Explain why pus forms at the site of infection: _____

    _____

© BIOZONE International 2007
ISBN: 978-1-877462-13-9
Photocopying Prohibited

Related activities: The Body's Defences, The Action of Phagocytes

Fever

Fever is a medical symptom that describes an increase in internal body temperature to levels that are above normal (36.2 to 37.2°C). Up to a point, fever is beneficial, since it assists a number of the defence processes. The release of the protein **interleukin-1** aids in resetting the body's thermostat to a higher level and helps step up the production of **T cells** (lymphocytes). Fever also intensifies the effect of the anti-viral protein **interferon** and is believed to inhibit the growth of some bacteria and viruses. It increases heart rate so that white blood cells are delivered to sites of infection more rapidly and may assist more rapid tissue repair by speeding up metabolic reactions. Fevers of less than 40°C do not need treatment for **hyperthermia**, but excessive fever requires prompt attention (particularly in children). Death usually results if body temperature rises to 44.4 to 45.5°C.

Defence & the Immune System

1. Discuss the beneficial effects of fever on the body's ability to fight infections: _____

   _____

   _____

   _____

2. Summarise the key steps of how the body's thermostat is set at a higher level by infection: _____

   _____

   _____

   _____

Related activities: The Body's Defences

A 2

The Lymphatic System

Fluid leaks out from capillaries and forms the tissue fluid, which is similar in composition to plasma but lacks large proteins. This fluid bathes the tissues, supplying them with nutrients and oxygen, and removing wastes. Some tissue fluid returns directly into the capillaries, but some drains back into general circulation through a network of lymph vessels. This fluid, called **lymph**, is similar to tissue fluid, but contains more leucocytes. Apart from its circulatory role, the lymphatic system has an important function in the immune response. Lymph nodes are the primary sites where pathogens and other foreign substances are destroyed. A lymph node that is fighting an infection becomes swollen and hard as the lymph cells reproduce rapidly to increase their numbers. The thymus, spleen, and bone marrow also contribute leucocytes to the lymphatic and circulatory systems.

1. Briefly describe the composition of lymph: _____

_____

2. Discuss the various roles of lymph: _____

_____

_____

3. State one role of each of the following in the lymphatic system:

    (a) Lymph nodes: _____

    (b) Bone marrow: _____

© BIOZONE International 2007
ISBN: 978-1-877462-13-9
Photocopying Prohibited

Related activities: The Immune System

The Immune System

The efficient internal defence provided by the immune system is based on its ability to respond specifically against a foreign substance and its ability to hold a memory of this response. There are two main components of the immune system: the humoral and the cell-mediated responses. They work separately and together to protect us from disease. The **humoral immune response** is associated with the serum (non-cellular part of the blood) and involves the action of **antibodies** secreted by B cell lymphocytes. Antibodies are found in extracellular fluids including lymph, plasma, and mucus secretions. The humoral response protects the body against circulating viruses, and bacteria and their toxins. The **cell-mediated immune response** is associated with the production of specialised lymphocytes called **T cells**. It is most effective against bacteria and viruses located within host cells, as well as against parasitic protozoa, fungi, and worms. This system is also an important defence against cancer, and is responsible for the rejection of transplanted tissue. Both B and T cells develop from stem cells located in the liver of fetuses and the bone marrow of adults. T cells complete their development in the thymus, whilst the B cells mature in the bone marrow.

Defence & the Immune System

Related activities: The Lymphatic System, Antibodies

A 2

The immune system has the ability to respond to the large and unpredictable range of potential antigens encountered in the environment. The diagram below explains how this ability is based on **clonal selection** after antigen exposure. The example illustrated is for B cell lymphocytes. In the same way, a T cell stimulated by a specific antigen will multiply and develop into different types of T cells. Clonal selection and differentiation of lymphocytes provide the basis for **immunological memory**.

ISBN: 978-1-877462-13-9

1. State the general action of the two major divisions in the immune system:

    (a) Humoral immune system: _____

    (b) Cell-mediated immune system: _____

2. Identify the origin of B cells and T cells (before maturing): _____

3. (a) Identify where B cells mature: _____ (b) Identify where T cells mature: _____

4. State briefly the function of each of the following cells in the immune system response:

    (a) Memory cells: _____

    (b) Plasma cells: _____

    (c) Helper T cells: _____

    (d) Suppressor T cells: _____

    (e) Delayed hypersensitivity T cells: _____

    (f) Cytotoxic T cells: _____

5. Briefly explain the basis of **immunological memory**: _____

    _____

    _____

    _____

Antibodies

Antibodies and antigens play key roles in the response of the immune system. Antigens are foreign molecules that are able to bind to antibodies (or T cell receptors) and provoke a specific immune response. Antigens include potentially damaging microbes and their toxins (see below) as well as substances such as pollen grains, blood cell surface molecules, and the surface proteins on transplanted tissues. **Antibodies** (also called immunoglobulins) are proteins that are made in response to antigens. They are secreted into the plasma where they circulate and can recognise, bind to, and help to destroy antigens. There are 5 classes of **immunoglobulins**. Each plays a different role in the immune response (including destroying protozoan parasites, enhancing phagocytosis, protecting mucous surfaces, and neutralising toxins and viruses). The human body can produce an estimated 100 million antibodies, recognising many different antigens, including those it has never encountered. Each type of antibody is highly specific to only one particular antigen. The ability of the immune system to recognise and ignore the antigenic properties of its own tissues occurs early in development and is called **self-tolerance**. Exceptions occur when the immune system malfunctions and the body attacks its own tissues, causing an **autoimmune disorder**.

Defence & the Immune System

© BIOZONE International 2007
ISBN: 978-1-877462-13-9
Photocopying Prohibited

Related activities: Targets for Defence, The Immune System, Acquired Immunity, Autoimmune Disease, Immunisation

RA 2

1. Distinguish between an antibody and an antigen: _____

_____

_____

_____

_____

_____

_____

_____

2. It is necessary for the immune system to clearly distinguish cells and proteins made by the body, from foreign ones.

   (a) Explain why this is the case: _____

   _____

   _____

   (b) In simple terms, explain how **self tolerance** develops (see the activity "The Immune System" if you need help):

   _____

   _____

   (c) Name the type of disorder that results when this recognition system fails: _____

   (d) Describe two examples of disorders that are caused in this way, identifying what happens in each case:

   _____

   _____

   _____

   _____

3. Discuss the ways in which antibodies work to inactivate antigens: _____

_____

_____

_____

_____

_____

_____

_____

_____

_____

_____

4. Explain how antibody activity enhances or leads to:

   (a) Phagocytosis: _____

   _____

   (b) Inflammation: _____

   _____

   (c) Bacterial cell lysis: _____

   _____

Acquired Immunity

We have natural or **innate resistance** to certain illnesses; examples include most diseases of other animal species. **Acquired immunity** refers to the protection an animal develops against certain types of microbes or foreign substances. Immunity can be acquired either passively or actively and is developed during an individual's lifetime. **Active immunity** develops when a person is exposed to microorganisms or foreign substances and the immune system responds. **Passive immunity** is acquired when antibodies are transferred from one person to another. Recipients do not make the antibodies themselves and the effect lasts only as long as the antibodies are present, usually several weeks or months. Immunity may also be **naturally acquired**, through natural exposure to microbes, or **artificially acquired** as a result of medical treatment.

1. (a) Explain what is meant by **active immunity**: _____

_____

(b) Distinguish between naturally and artificially acquired active immunity and give an example of each:

_____

_____

2. (a) Explain what is meant by **passive immunity**: _____

_____

(b) Distinguish between naturally and artificially acquired passive immunity and give an example of each:

_____

_____

3. Prior to birth, a baby receives antibodies across the placenta from its mother.
(a) Explain why a newborn baby needs to have had a supply of maternal antibodies: _____

_____

(b) Explain why this supply is supplemented by antibodies provided in breast milk: _____

_____

Related activities: Immunisation

A 2

Defence & the Immune System

Autoimmune Diseases

Any of numerous disorders, including **rheumatoid arthritis**, insulin dependent **diabetes mellitus**, and **multiple sclerosis**, are caused by an individual's immune system reaction to their own cells or tissues. The immune system normally distinguishes self from non-self. Some lymphocytes are capable of reacting against self, but these are generally suppressed. **Autoimmune diseases** occur when there is some interruption of the normal control process, allowing lymphocytes to escape from suppression, or when there is an alteration in some body tissue so that it is no longer recognised as self. The exact mechanisms behind autoimmune malfunctions are not fully understood but pathogens or drugs may play a role in triggering an autoimmune response in someone who already has a genetic predisposition. The reactions are similar to those that occur in allergies, except that in autoimmune disorders, the the hypersensitivity response is to the body itself, rather than to an outside substance.

1. Explain the basis of the following autoimmune diseases:

   (a) Multiple sclerosis: _____

   _____

   (b) Rheumatoid arthritis: _____

   _____

2. Suggest why autoimmune diseases are difficult to treat effectively: _____

   _____

   _____

3. Explain why sufferers of immune deficiencies, such as AIDS, develop a range of debilitating infections:

   _____

   _____

© BIOZONE International 2007
ISBN: 978-1-877462-13-9
Photocopying Prohibited

The Homeostatic Role of Blood

Blood makes up about 8% of body weight. Blood is a complex liquid tissue comprising cellular components suspended in plasma. If a blood sample is taken, the cells can be separated from the plasma by centrifugation. The cells (formed elements) settle as a dense red pellet below the transparent, straw-coloured plasma. Blood performs many functions: it transports nutrients, respiratory gases, hormones, and wastes; it has a role in thermoregulation through the distribution of heat; it defends against infection; and its ability to clot protects against blood loss. The examination of blood is also useful in diagnosing disease. The cellular components of blood are normally present in particular specified ratios. A change in the morphology, type, or proportion of different blood cells can therefore be used to indicate a specific disorder or infection (right).

Defence & the Immune System

Related activities: Blood Clotting and Defence, The Body's defences

A 2

1. For each of the following homeostatic functions of blood, identify the component (or components) of the blood responsible and state how the function is carried out (the mode of action). The first one is done for you:

   (a) **Temperature regulation**. *Blood component:* Water component of the plasma

   Mode of action: Water absorbs heat and dissipates it from sites of production (e.g. organs)

   (b) **Protection against disease**. *Blood component:* _____

   Mode of action: _____

   (c) **Communication between cells, tissues, and organs**. *Blood component:* _____

   Mode of action: _____

   (d) **Oxygen transport**. *Blood component:* _____

   Mode of action: _____

   (e) **CO$_2$ transport**. *Blood components:* _____

   Mode of action: _____

   (f) **Buffer against pH changes**. *Blood components:* _____

   Mode of action: _____

   (g) **Nutrient supply**. *Blood component:* _____

   Mode of action: _____

   (h) **Tissue repair**. *Blood components:* _____

   Mode of action: _____

   (i) **Transport of hormones, lipids, and fat soluble vitamins**. *Blood component:* _____

   Mode of action: _____

2. Identify a feature that distinguishes red and white blood cells: _____

3. Explain two physiological advantages of red blood cell structure (lacking nucleus and mitochondria):

   (a) _____

   (b) _____

4. Suggest what each of the following results from a differential white blood cell count would suggest:

   (a) Elevated levels of eosinophils (above the normal range): _____

   (b) Elevated levels of neutrophils (above the normal range): _____

   (c) Elevated levels of basophils (above the normal range): _____

   (d) Elevated levels of lymphocytes (above the normal range): _____

© BIOZONE International 2007
ISBN: 978-1-877462-13-9
Photocopying Prohibited

Allergies and Hypersensitivity

Sometimes the immune system may overreact, or react to the wrong substances instead of responding appropriately. This is termed **hypersensitivity** and the immunological response leads to tissue damage rather than immunity. Hypersensitivity reactions occur after a person has been **sensitised** to an antigen. In some cases, this causes only localised discomfort, as in the case of hayfever. More generalised reactions (such as anaphylaxis from insect venom or drug injections), or localised reactions that affect essential body systems (such as asthma), can cause death through asphyxiation and/or circulatory shock.

Defence & the Immune System

1. Explain the role of histamine in hypersensitivity responses: _____

_____

2. Explain what is meant by becoming **sensitised** to an allergen: _____

_____

3. Explain the effect of **bronchodilators** and explain why they are used to treat asthma: _____

_____

Related activities: The Immune System, Autoimmune Diseases

RA 2

Non-Infectious Disease

The nature and range of non-infectious disease

Health vs disease: genetic, degenerative, nutritional , and social diseases (including the effects of tobacco and substance abuse).

Learning Objectives

☐ 1. Compile your own glossary from the **KEY WORDS** displayed in **bold type** in the learning objectives below.

Non-infectious Disease *(page 30, 33, 57-58)*

☐ 2. Explain what is meant by a **non-infectious disease**. Identify and classify examples of non-infectious diseases as: • Nutritional (deficiency) diseases • Genetic (congenital) diseases • Environmental (social) diseases • Mental diseases • Degenerative diseases • Diseases of physiological malfunction e.g. enzyme and hormonal disorders • Autoimmune diseases.

☐ 3. Recognise that diseases may result from a combination of environmental, hereditary, and biological factors.

☐ 4. Using an named example of a non-infectious disease, identify and describe the main features of **epidemiology**.

☐ 5. Identify causes of non-infectious diseases, using an example from each of: **inherited disease, nutritional deficiency**, and **social disease**. You may wish to use the examples described below (#6-28).

Genetic Diseases *(pages 49-52)*

☐ 6. Explain what is meant by a **genetic disease**. Name some genetic diseases, and describe their symptoms and their origin (genetic basis). Examples could include:
   (a) **Sickle cell disease**
   (b) **Cystic fibrosis**
   (c) **Huntington disease**
   (d) Trisomic disorders, such as **Down syndrome**

☐ 7. Explain what is meant by the **maternal age effect**. Describe an example of a chromosomal disorder that shows a maternal age effect.

Degenerative Diseases *(pages 35-36, 41)*

☐ 8. Identify the physiological basis of **ageing**. Describe measures to delay the onset of degenerative disease and evaluate their effectiveness.

☐ 9. Describe some of the **degenerative diseases** of ageing, including their symptoms and physiological basis. Include reference to any of the following:
   (a) **Alzheimer's disease** (senile dementia)
   (b) **Osteoarthritis**
   (c) **Osteoporosis**
   (d) **Cataracts** and **hypermetropia** (far-sightedness)

Nutritional Diseases *(pages 42-44, 93-94)*

☐ 10. Explain clearly what is meant by a **nutritional disease**. Distinguish between **starvation, malnutrition**, and **deficiency disease** (e.g. vitamin of mineral deficiency).

☐ 11. Describe the causes, diagnosis, symptoms, and treatment of different types of **malnutrition** with reference to some or all of the following:
   (a) Energy and protein deficiency
   (b) **Anorexia nervosa** and/or bulimia nervosa
   (c) **Obesity** and/or excessive intake of fat and salt
   (d) Deficiency of vitamins A and D
   (e) Deficiency of vitamin C and (named) mineral ions.

☐ 12. Evaluate the evidence for the possible links between diet and **coronary heart disease**.

Social Diseases

Smoking and disease *(pages 31-32, 37)*

☐ 13. Explain the role of **tobacco** as a cause of preventable disease. Provide statistics for the number of deaths directly or indirectly related to tobacco smoking.

☐ 14. Document the history of cigarette smoking in the western world and comment on the addictiveness of cigarettes compared with other forms of tobacco.

☐ 15. List the constituents of cigarette smoke and describe the effects of the **tars** and **carcinogens** in tobacco smoke on the respiratory and cardiovascular systems. Identify the addictive component of tobacco.

☐ 16. Describe the physiological effects of cigarette smoking. List and describe the symptoms of some diseases directly or indirectly associated with tobacco smoking: chronic **bronchitis, emphysema, lung cancer**, and **cardiovascular disease**.

☐ 17. Evaluate the epidemiological and experimental evidence linking cigarette smoking to the incidence of disease and early death.

☐ 18. Describe the short and long term effects of cigarette smoking and list the factors that increase its harmful effects. Describe what is meant by **passive smoking** and comment on its effects on non-smokers. Describe the detrimental health effects of smoking in pregnancy.

Drug abuse *(page 48)*

☐ 19. Define the terms: **drug** and **drug abuse**. Distinguish between recreational drugs, medicinal drugs, and food supplements (e.g. vitamins, bee pollen, spirulina).

☐ 20. Describe the derivation, active ingredient, and physiological effects of some commonly used drugs.

Physiological Malfunction with Multiple Causes

Diabetes mellitus *(pages 46-47, 90, 109)*

☐ 21. Distinguish between **type 1** (juvenile onset) and **type 2** (adult onset) **diabetes mellitus**. Discuss their causes, symptoms, severity, and treatment.

☐ 22. Contrast the treatment for juvenile onset diabetes with the treatment for adult onset diabetes.

Cancers *(pages 37-40)*

☐ 23. Define the terms **cancer**, **tumour**, and **carcinogen**. Discuss some of the known causes of cancers and their effects. Recognise the involvement of environmental, hereditary, and biological factors in the development of cancers.

☐ 24. Explain how carcinogens promote cancer through damage to the DNA and loss of the normal controls over cell division.

☐ 25. Distinguish between **benign** and **malignant tumours**. Explain why some cancers spread (undergo **metastasis**) more rapidly than others.

☐ 26. Provide details of the development, **symptoms**, **diagnosis**, **treatment**, and **prognosis** for one type of cancer. Consider the effectiveness of treatments

generally available for cancer. Discuss the role of early detection in more effective cancer control.

Cardiovascular disease *(pages 31, 33-34, 119)*

☐ 27. Recognise the term **cardiovascular disease** (CVD), as a broad term encompassing a variety of diseases. Distinguish between some of the different forms of CVD, e.g. **atherosclerosis** and **hypertension**.

☐ 28. Outline stages in the development of **atherosclerosis**. Describe the factors implicated in the development of atherosclerosis e.g. tobacco smoking, lack of exercise, **obesity**, high blood pressure, poor dietary habits.

☐ 29. Describe the **epidemiology** of cardiovascular diseases, particularly coronary heart disease. Relate their global pattern of occurrence to lifestyle factors.

See page 7 for additional details of this text:

■ Fullick, A., 2000. **Human Health and Disease** (Heinemann), chpt. 1, 3-6.

■ Murray, P. & N. Owens, 2001. **Behaviour and Populations** (Collins), chpt. 8.

See page 7 for details of publishers of periodicals:

STUDENT'S REFERENCE

Non-infectious causes of cancer

Note that infectious agents are increasingly implicated in the development of cancers.

■ **What is Cancer?** Biol. Sci. Rev., 11(1) Sept. 1998, pp. 38-41. *The cellular basis of cancer, with a look at some new ways to combat the disease.*

■ **Cancer: What is it and how is it Treated?** Biol. Sci. Rev., 16(1) Sept. 2003, pp. 26-30. *An account of the characteristics of cancer, how it arises, and strategies in cancer treatment.*

■ **Out of Control - Unlocking the Genetic Secrets of Cancer** Biol. Sci. Rev., 11(3) January 1999, pp. 38-41. *A look at the failures in gene regulation that lead to the development of cancer.*

■ **Rebels without a Cause** New Scientist, 13 July 2002, (Inside Science). *The causes of cancer: the uncontrolled division of cells that results in tumour formation. Breast cancer is the case study given.*

Cardiovascular & respiratory diseases

■ **Heart Attacks** New Scientist , 12 June 1993, (Inside Science). *The nature of heart attacks and the epidemiology of heart disease.*

■ **Coronary Heart Disease** Biol. Sci. Rev., 18(1) Sept. 2005, pp. 21-24. An account of cardiovascular disease, including risk factors and treatments.

■ **Heart Disease and Cholesterol** Biol. Sci. Rev., 13(2) Nov. 2000, pp. 2-5. *The links between dietary fat, cholesterol level, and heart disease.*

■ **Environmental Lung Disease** New Scientist, 23 September 1995 (Inside Science). *Diseases of the lungs and cardiovascular system.*

■ **Smoking** Biol. Sci. Rev. 10(1) Sept. 1997, pp. 14-16. *The effects on human physiology of tobacco smoking, including the types and symptoms of smoking related diseases.*

■ **Mending Broken Hearts** Nat. Geographic, 211(2) 2007, pp. 40-65. *Heart disease, its causes & treatments including artificial heart replacement.*

Dietary and metabolic diseases

■ **Lactose Intolerance** Biol. Sci. Rev., 17(3), Feb. 2005, pp. 28-31. *The nature of lactose intolerance (the inability to digest milk). Rather than an allergy, this disorder is a physiological response following a genetically programmed loss of lactase.*

■ **Supersized Surprise** New Scientist, 4 Nov. 2006, pp. 34-38. *Summarises then major reasons why obesity is becoming an epidemic.*

■ **Leptin** Biol. Sci. Rev., 15(3), Feb. 2003, pp. 30-32. *The role of the hormone leptin in regulating body mass and controlling obesity.*

■ **Diabetes** Biol. Sci. Rev., 15(2) November 2002, pp. 30-35. *The nature of Type I diabetes: symptoms, complications, monitoring and control of the disease. This account includes details of the structure of the endocrine portion of the pancreas.*

■ **Obesity: Size Matters** Biol. Sci. Rev., 18(4) April 2006, pp. 10-13. *An account of obesity and the health issues surrounding it.*

■ **Eating Disorders: Myths and Misconceptions** Biol. Sci. Rev., 9(5) May 1997, pp. 25-27. *The causes and treatments of eating disorders.*

■ **Vital Vitamins** Biol. Sci. Rev., 11(5) May 1999, pp. 32-35. *The role of vitamins in the diet, including the diseases caused by vitamin deficiencies.*

■ **Hard Cheese** New Scientist, 15 December 2001, pp. 42-45. *It seems that the modern 'healthy' diet may be bad for bone development and maintenance, accelerating degenerative disease.*

■ **How to Defy Death** New Scientist, 25 March 2000, pp. 20-23. *How can diet promote longevity? Eating less may slow cellular damage.*

■ **The Good, the Fad and the Unhealthy** New Scientist, 27 Sept, 2006, pp. 42-49. *The facts, the myths, and the downright lies of nutrition.*

Degenerative diseases

■ **The Biology of Ageing** Biol. Sci. Rev., 10(3) January 1998, pp. 18-21. *Ageing and degenerative disease (includes Alzheimer's and its pathology).*

■ **Unravelling the Mysteries of Human Ageing** Biol. Sci. Rev., 14(3) February 2002, pp. 33-37. *The physiology of human ageing and an account of age related diseases and disabilities.*

■ **Aging** National Geographic, 192(5), Nov. 1997, pp. 2-31. *An account of the physiological aspects of aging as well as the social issues of elderly care.*

■ **Age - Old Story** New Scientist, 23 Jan. 1999, (Inside Science). *The processes involved in aging.*

TEACHER'S REFERENCE

■ **Everyday Exposure to Toxic Pollutants** Scientific American, Feb. 1998, pp. 72-77. *How toxic pollutants, chemicals, and air pollution pose a risk of cancer, allergies, and respiratory diseases.*

■ **The Cancer Revolution** New Scientist, 23 August 2003, pp. 36-39. *The use of DNA microarrays to identify the genes responsible for causing cancer. Gene activity signatures could then be used to predict whether a tumour is likely to spread to other parts of the body.*

■ **Untangling the Roots of Cancer** New Scientist, July 2003, pp. 48-57. *How do cells become malignant? This article includes a diagram to explain theories of cancer development.*

■ **What You Need to Know About Cancer** SPECIAL ISSUE: Scientific American, Sept. 1996, entire issue. *Thorough coverage of the genetic and environmental causes of various cancers: symptoms, prevention, detection, and therapies.*

■ **Obesity: An Overblown Epidemic?** Scientific American, June 2005, pp. 48-55. *Arguments for and against the conventional wisdom linking obesity to increased incidence of disease.*

■ **Atherosclerosis: The New View** Scientific American, May 2002, pp. 28-37. *The latest views on the pathological development and rupture of plaques in atherosclerosis. Excellent.*

■ **Dark Angel** New Scientist, 18 Dec. 2004, pp. 38-41. *An account of the p53 gene and the role of its expressed protein in the prevention and triggering of cancers.*

■ **Piecing Together Alzheimer's** Sci. American, Dec. 2000, pp. 52-59. *An excellent account of the physiology and pathology of this common disease.*

■ **Alcohol in the Western World** Scientific American, June 1998, pp. 62-67. *The changing perception of alcohol throughout western civilisation, with a look at the effects on human physiology of excessive alcohol intake.*

■ **Gaining on Fat** Scientific American, August 1996, pp. 70-76. *Discovering the biological roots of obesity and the hope of new treatments.*

See pages 4-5 for details of how to access **Bio Links** from our web site: **www.thebiozone.com** From Bio Links, access sites under the topics:

HEALTH & DISEASE: • CDC disease links • NewsFile • WHO/OMS: health topics > **Non-Infectious Diseases:** • Asthma • Chemicals and human health • Your genes: your health • FAQ about diabetes • Smoking and your digestive system • Breast cancer screening • Cancer • Cancer Research UK • NCI's Cancernet • Cardiology compass • Heart disease *.. and many others* > **Human Health Issues:** • Eating disorders • British Nutrition Foundation • The effects of drugs on the human body *... and others*

GENETICS > Mutations and Genetic Disorders: Blazing a genetic trail • Your genes: your health • Cystic fibrosis • PKU fact sheet • Facts about cystic fibrosis... *and others*

Presentation MEDIA to support this topic:

HEALTH & DISEASE:
• **The Nature of Disease**
• **Non-Infectious Disease**

Non-Infectious Disease

Health vs Disease

Disease is more difficult to define than **health**, which is described as a state of complete physical, mental, and social well-being. A disease is usually associated with particular **symptoms** that help to define and diagnose it. The term **disease** is used to describe a condition whereby part or all of an organism's normal physiological function is upset. All diseases, with the exception of some mental diseases, can be classified as **physical diseases** (i.e. diseases that cause permanent or temporary damage to the body). Physical diseases can be subdivided into two major groups: **infectious diseases** caused by an infectious agent (**pathogen**) and **non-infectious diseases** (most of which are better described as disorders). Non-infectious diseases are often not clearly the result of any single factor, but they can be further categorised into major subgroups according to their principal cause (outlined below). However, many diseases fall into more than one category, e.g. Alzheimer's disease and some cancers.

1. Discuss the differences between health and disease: _____

_____

_____

_____

2. Using illustrative examples, explain why many diseases fall into more than one disease category:

_____

_____

Related activities: Infection and Disease

© BIOZONE International 2007
ISBN: 978-1-877462-13-9
Photocopying Prohibited

Diseases Caused by Smoking

Tobacco smoking has only recently been accepted as a major health hazard, despite its practice in developed countries for more than 400 years, and much longer elsewhere. Cigarettes became popular at the end of World War I because they were cheap, convenient, and easier to smoke than pipes and cigars. They remain popular for the further reason that they are more addictive than other forms of tobacco. The milder smoke can be more readily inhaled, allowing **nicotine** (a powerful addictive poison) to be quickly absorbed into the bloodstream. **Lung cancer** is the most widely known and most harmful effect of smoking. Tobacco smoking is also directly associated with coronary artery disease, emphysema, chronic bronchitis, peripheral vascular disease, and stroke. Despite recent indications that smoking-related mortality may be declining in developed countries, one third of all deaths from cancer, including around 90% of lung cancer deaths, are linked to this cause. The damaging components of cigarette smoke include tar, carbon monoxide, nitrogen dioxide, and nitric oxide. Many of these chemicals occur in greater concentrations in sidestream smoke (**passive smoking**) than in mainstream smoke (inhaled) due to the presence of a filter in the cigarette.

Non-Infectious Disease

Related activities: Cancer, Cardiovascular Disease

RDA 2

Components of Cigarette Smoke

Particulate Phase

Nicotine: a highly addictive alkaloid

Tar: composed of many chemicals

Benzene: carcinogenic hydrocarbon

Gas Phase

Carbon monoxide: a poisonous gas

Ammonia: a pungent, colourless gas

Formaldehyde: a carcinogen

Hydrogen cyanide: a highly poisonous gas

Tobacco smoke is made up of "sidestream smoke" from the burning tip and "mainstream smoke" from the filter (mouth) end. Sidestream smoke contains higher concentrations of many toxins than mainstream smoke. Tobacco smoke includes both particulate and gas phases (left), both of which contain many harmful substances.

Filter
Cellulose acetate filters trap some of the tar and smoke particles. They cool the smoke slightly, making it easier to inhale.

1. Discuss the physical changes to the lung that result from long-term smoking:

2. Determine the physiological effect of each of the following constituents of tobacco smoke when inhaled:

   (a) Tar:

   (b) Nicotine:

   (c) Carbon monoxide:

3. Describe the symptoms of the following diseases associated with long-term smoking:

   (a) Emphysema:

   (b) Chronic bronchitis:

   (c) Lung cancer:

4. Evaluate the evidence linking cigarette smoking to deleterious effects on health:

Cardiovascular Disease

Cardiovascular disease (CVD) is a term describing all diseases involving the heart and blood vessels. It includes coronary heart disease (CHD), atherosclerosis, hypertension (high blood pressure), peripheral vascular disease, stroke, and congenital heart disorders. CVD is responsible for 20% of all deaths worldwide and is the principal cause of deaths in developed countries. Since the 1970s, deaths due to CVD have been declining as a result of better prevention and treatment. Despite this, CVD is still a leading cause of mortality. Its continued prevalence is of considerable public health concern, particularly as many of the **risk factors** involved, including cigarette smoking, obesity, and high blood cholesterol, are controllable. Uncontrollable risk factors include advancing age, gender, and heredity (inherited susceptibility).

Non-Infectious Disease

Related activities: Diseases Caused by Smoking

RDA 3

1. Explain briefly how atherosclerosis leads to death of heart tissue and a heart attack (infarct): _____
   _____
   _____

2. Mortality attributable to CVD is declining, despite its increasing prevalence. Suggest why: _____
   _____

3. (a) From the graph on the previous page, determine the proportion of CVD deaths occurring in females and males in England and Wales:

   Females: _____   Males: _____

   (b) Suggest a possible reason for this difference: _____
   _____

4. Suggest possible alternative reasons, other than diet, for the global distribution of CVD: _____
   _____
   _____
   _____

5. (a) Distinguish between controllable and uncontrollable risk factors in the development of CVD: _____
   _____
   _____

   (b) Suggest why some of the controllable risk factors often occur together: _____
   _____

   (c) Explain why patients with several risk factors have a much higher risk of developing CVD: _____
   _____

6. (a) Choose one of the controllable risk factors listed above, and describe its role in the development of CVD:
   _____
   _____
   _____

   (b) Suggest how the risk (of CVD) presented by this factor could be reduced: _____
   _____

Degenerative Disease

After attaining physical maturity, the body undergoes a number of **degenerative changes** collectively known as senescence or **ageing**. Ageing results in a progressive failure of the body's homeostatic responses, occurring as a result of cells dying and renewal rates slowing or stopping. It is a general response, producing observable changes in structure and physiology, for example, reduced immune function, a decline in skeletal and muscular strength, and a reduction in the speed of neural processing. Ageing increases susceptibility to stress and disease, and disease and ageing often accelerate together.

Non-Infectious Disease

1. Briefly explain what causes ageing of the body, carefully relating the physiological changes to the observable effects:

_____

_____

_____

2. Name and describe two degenerative diseases or disorders, including reference to symptoms and physiological causes:

(a) _____

_____

_____

_____

RA 2

(b) _____

_____

_____

_____

_____

_____

3. Suggest how weight-bearing exercise could delay the onset of ageing: _____

_____

_____

_____

4. Some loss of neuronal function occurs normally as a result of ageing. Identify the features distinguishing Alzheimer's disease from normal age related loss of neuronal function:

_____

_____

_____

_____

ISBN: 978-1-877462-13-9

Cancer

Cancer is a term describing a large group of diseases characterised by the progressive and uncontrolled growth of abnormal cells. Cancer is not a new disease, nor is it restricted just to humans. Most other animals suffer from cancer; evidence of it has even been found in the fossilised bones of dinosaurs. There is no single cause for all the forms of cancer; environmental, genetic, and biological factors may all be involved. Although the incidence of cancer has apparently increased in more recent times, this may simply reflect our increased life spans, as the incidence of many cancers increases with age. Of all cancer deaths, nearly half are caused by just four cancers (lung, bowel, breast, and prostate).

1. Briefly describe the characteristics of the following stages of a developing cancer:

(a) Benign tumour: _____

_____

(b) Malignant tumour: _____

_____

_____

Related activities: Diseases Caused by Smoking, Breast Cancer, The Genetic Origins of Cancer

A 2

Non-Infectious Disease

(c) Metastasis: _____

_____

2. Explain how the following treatments work to destroy cancerous tumours (while leaving healthy tissue less affected):

(a) Chemotherapy: _____

_____

_____

(b) Radiotherapy: _____

_____

_____

3. (a) Describe some of the unwanted (harmful) side effects of these two treatments (above):

_____

_____

(b) Explain why these side effects happen: _____

_____

4. List the probable causes and characteristic symptoms associated with the following types of cancer:

(a) Causes of skin cancer: _____

Symptoms: _____

_____

(b) Causes of lung cancer: _____

Symptoms: _____

_____

Breast Cancer

Breast cancer is by far the most common cancer in women, affecting more than 1 million women worldwide. More than 25% of all female cancers occur in the breast, and the incidence increases with age, with 80% of cases occurring in post menopausal women. Fewer than 1% of breast cancer cases occur in men. Female sex hormones are implicated in the development of many breast cancers. The incidence of the disease is higher in women who began menstruation early and/ or whose menopause was late. Women who have no children or who had their first child when they were in their late 20s or 30s (or older) are also at higher risk. There is also a definite **familial** (heredity) factor in many cases. A high fat diet is also implicated. In Japan, where a low fat diet is typical, the disease is rare. Yet Japanese women living in the United States and eating a higher-fat American diet have the same rate of breast cancer as American women generally.

Non-Infectious Disease

1. Describe three factors associated with increased risk of developing breast cancer and suggest why they increase risk:

   _____

   _____

2. Suggest in what way breast self examination may be deficient in detecting early breast cancers: _____

   _____

3. Describe a possible treatment for early breast cancer involving a small isolated tumour: _____

   _____

4. State the evidence for a link between diet and increased risk of developing breast cancer: _____

   _____

   _____

Related activities: Cancer

A 2

The Genetic Origins of Cancer

Normal cells do not live forever. Under certain circumstances, cells are programmed to die, particularly during development. Cells that become damaged beyond repair will normally undergo this programmed cell death (called **apoptosis** or **cell suicide**). Cancer cells evade this control and become immortal, continuing to divide regardless of any damage incurred. **Carcinogens** are agents capable of causing cancer. Roughly 90% of carcinogens are also mutagens, i.e. they damage DNA. Chronic exposure to carcinogens accelerates the rate at which dividing cells make errors. Susceptibility to cancer is also influenced by genetic make-up. Any one or a number of cancer-causing factors (including defective genes) may interact to induce cancer.

1. Explain how cancerous cells differ from normal cells: _____

_____

2. Explain how the cell cycle is normally controlled, including reference to the role of **tumour-suppressor genes**:

_____

_____

_____

_____

3. With reference to the role of **oncogenes**, explain how the normal controls over the cell cycle can be lost:

_____

_____

_____

© BIOZONE International 2007
ISBN: 978-1-877462-13-9
Photocopying Prohibited

A 2

Related activities: Cancer, Breast Cancer

The lens of the eye has two convex surfaces (biconvex). When light enters the eye, the lens bends the incoming rays towards each other so that they intersect at the focal point on the central fovea of the retina. By altering the curvature of the lens, the focusing power of the eye can be adjusted. This adjustment of the eye for near or far vision is called **accommodation** and it is possible because of the elasticity of the lens. For some people, the shape of the eyeball or the lens prevents convergence of the light rays on the central fovea, and images are focused in front of, or behind, the retina. Such visual defects (below) can be corrected with specific lenses. As we age, the lens loses some of its elasticity and, therefore, its ability to accommodate. This inability to focus on nearby objects due to loss of lens elasticity is a natural part of ageing and is called **far sight**.

Non-Infectious Disease

1. With respect to formation of the image, describe what is happening in:

    (a) Short sighted people: _____

    (b) Long sighted people: _____

2. In general terms, describe how the use of lenses corrects the following problems associated with vision:

    (a) Myopia: _____

    (b) Hypermetropia: _____

3. Explain how accommodation of the eye for near and distant vision is achieved: _____

    _____

    _____

Dietary Disorders

Most forms of malnutrition in western societies are the result of poorly balanced nutrient intakes rather than a lack of food *per se*. Dietary disorders may arise as a result of overeating (**obesity**), insufficient food intake (**anorexia nervosa**), or abnormally erratic eating habits (**bulimia nervosa**). Other health problems typically prevalent in western societies, including **cardiovascular diseases**, have been associated to varying degrees with the consumption of highly processed foods, high in cholesterol and saturated fats. Low fibre intake is a factor in the development of **colon cancer**, while high salt intake may lead to **hypertension**.

1. Describe the two basic energy factors that determine how a person's weight will change: _____
   _____

2. Using the BMI, calculate the minimum and maximum weight at which a 1.85 m tall man would be considered:

   (a) Overweight: _____   (c) Obese: _____

   (b) Normal weight: _____   (d) Underweight: _____

3. State the possible health consequences of the following aspects of a diet:

   (a) High salt consumption: _____

   (b) Low fibre content: _____

   (c) High cholesterol content: _____

4. Identify the key differences between anorexia nervosa and bulimia nervosa: _____
   _____
   _____

© BIOZONE International 2007
ISBN: 978-1-877462-13-9
Photocopying Prohibited

Related activities: Deficiency Diseases, A Balanced Diet, Type 2 Diabetes, The Health Benefits of Exercise

Deficiency Diseases

Malnutrition is the general term for nutritional disorders resulting from not having enough food (starvation), not enough of the right food (deficiency), or too much food (obesity). Children under 5 are the most at risk from starvation and deficiency diseases because they are growing rapidly and are more susceptible to disease. Malnutrition is a key factor in the deaths of 6 million children each year and, in developing countries, dietary deficiencies are a major problem. In these countries, malnutrition usually presents as **marasmus** or **kwashiorkor** (energy and protein deficiencies).

Specific vitamin and mineral deficiencies (below and following) are often associated with specific diseases, e.g. beriberi (vitamin B_1), scurvy (vitamin C), rickets (vitamin D), pellagra (niacin), or anaemia (iron). Vitamin deficiencies in childhood result in chronic, lifelong disorders. Deficiency diseases are rare in developed countries. People who do suffer from some form of dietary deficiency are either alcoholics, people with intestinal disorders that prevent proper nutrient uptake, or people with very restricted diets (e.g. vegans).

Non-Infectious Disease

1. Distinguish between **malnutrition** and **starvation**: _____

_____

_____

_____

2. For each of the following vitamins, identify the natural sources of the vitamin, its function, and effect of deficiency:

   (a) Vitamin A: _____

   Function: _____

   Deficiency: _____

   (b) Vitamin B_{12}: _____

   Function: _____

   Deficiency: _____

Related activities: Dietary Disorders, A Balanced Diet

RA 2

44

(c) Vitamin C: _____

   Function: _____

   Deficiency: _____

(d) Vitamin D: _____

   Function: _____

   Deficiency: _____

3. Suggest why young children, pregnant women, and athletes are among the most susceptible to dietary deficiencies:

   _____

   _____

   _____

   _____

4. Explain why a lack of iron leads to the symptoms of anaemia (fatigue and breathlessness): _____

   _____

   _____

5. Suggest why a zinc deficiency is associated with muscular weakness and a delay in puberty: _____

   _____

   _____

6. Suggest why table salt is often iodised: _____

   _____

7. Explain why people suffering from nutritional deficiencies have a poor resistance to disease: _____

   _____

   _____

   _____

   _____

© BIOZONE International 2007
ISBN: 978-1-877462-13-9
Photocopying Prohibited

Control of Blood Glucose

The endocrine portions of the **pancreas**, specifically the alpha and beta cells of the **islets of Langerhans**, produce two hormones, **insulin** and **glucagon**. Together, these hormones mediate the regulation of blood glucose, maintaining a steady state through **negative feedback**. Insulin promotes a decrease in blood glucose through synthesis of glycogen and cellular uptake of glucose. Glucagon promotes an increase in blood glucose through the breakdown of glycogen and the synthesis of glucose from amino acids. Restoration of normal blood glucose level acts through negative feedback to stop hormone secretion. Regulating blood glucose to within narrow limits allows energy to be available to cells as needed. Extra energy is stored, as glycogen or fat, and is mobilised to meet energy needs as required. The liver is pivotal in these carbohydrate conversions.

Non-Infectious Disease

1. (a) Identify the stimulus for the release of insulin: _____

   (b) Identify the stimulus for the release of glucagon: _____

   (c) Explain how glucagon brings about an increase in blood glucose level: _____
   _____

   (d) Explain how insulin brings about a decrease in blood glucose level: _____
   _____

2. Outline the role of negative feedback in the control of blood glucose: _____
   _____

3. Explain why fats are metabolised after a long period without food: _____
   _____

Related activities: Type 1 Diabetes, Type 2 Diabetes

A 2

Type 1 Diabetes

Diabetes is a general term for a range of disorders sharing two common symptoms: production of large amounts of urine and excessive thirst. Other symptoms depend on the type of diabetes. **Diabetes mellitus** is the most common form of diabetes and is characterised by **hyperglycemia** (high blood sugar). **Type 1** **diabetes** is characterised by a lack of insulin production and usually begins in childhood as a result of autoimmune destruction of the insulin producing cells of the pancreas. For this reason it is often called juvenile onset diabetes. It is a chronic, incurable condition, which is treated primarily with insulin injections.

1. Describe the **symptoms** of type 1 diabetes mellitus and relate these to the physiological cause of the disease:

   _____

   _____

   _____

   _____

2. Summarise the **treatments** for (list key words/phrases only):

   (a) Present treatment: _____

   (b) New treatments: _____

   (c) Future treatments: _____

A 2 **Related activities**: Control of Blood Glucose, Type 2 Diabetes

Type 2 Diabetes

Unlike type 1 diabetes, **type 2 diabetes** is more typically a disease of older, overweight people whose cells develop a resistance to insulin uptake. Type 2 sufferers manage their disease through diet and exercise in an attempt to limit the disease's long term detrimental effects. As with type 1 diabetes, the type 2 form is treatable but not curable, and insulin therapy may eventually be used to manage blood glucose levels if diet and lifestyle factors alone do not provide sufficient control.

Symptoms of Type 2 Diabetes Mellitus

a Symptoms may be mild at first. The body's cells do not respond appropriately to the insulin that is present and blood glucose levels become elevated. Normal blood glucose level is 60-110 mgdL^{-1}. In diabetics fasting blood glucose level is 126 mgdL^{-1} or higher.

b Symptoms occur with varying degrees of severity:
- Cells are starved of fuel. This can lead to increased appetite and overeating and may contribute to an existing obesity problem.
- Urine production increases to rid the body of the excess glucose. Glucose is present in the urine and patients are frequently very thirsty.
- The body's inability to use glucose properly leads to muscle weakness and fatigue, irritability, frequent infections, and poor wound healing.

c Uncontrolled elevated blood glucose eventually results in damage to the blood vessels and leads to:
- coronary artery disease
- peripheral vascular disease
- retinal damage, blurred vision and blindness
- kidney damage and renal failure
- persistent ulcers and gangrene

Risk Factors

Obesity: BMI greater than 27. Distribution of weight is also important.

Age: Risk increases with age, although the incidence of type 2 diabetes is increasingly reported in obese children.

Sedentary lifestyle: Inactivity increases risk through its effects on bodyweight.

Family history: There is a strong genetic link for type 2 diabetes. Those with a family history of the disease are at greater risk.

Ethnicity: Certain ethnic groups are at higher risk of developing of type 2 diabetes.

High blood pressure: Up to 60% of people with undiagnosed diabetes have high blood pressure.

High blood lipids: More than 40% of people with diabetes have abnormally high levels of cholesterol and similar lipids in the blood.

Treating Type 2 Diabetes

Diabetes is not curable but can be managed to minimise the health effects:
- Regularly check blood glucose level
- Manage diet to reduce fluctuations in blood glucose level
- Take regular exercise
- Reduce weight
- Reduce blood pressure
- Reduce or stop smoking
- Take prescribed anti-diabetic drugs
- In time, insulin therapy may be required

Cellular uptake of glucose is impaired and glucose enters the bloodstream instead. Type 2 diabetes is sometimes called **Insulin resistance**.

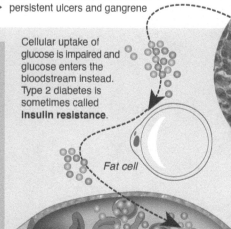

Fat cell

Insulin

The **beta cells** of the pancreatic islets (above) produce insulin, the hormone responsible for the cellular uptake of glucose. In type 2 diabetes, the body's cells do not utilise the insulin properly.

Non-Infectious Disease

1. Distinguish between type 1 and type 2 diabetes, relating the differences to the different methods of treatment:

2. Explain what dietary advice you would give to a person diagnosed with type 2 diabetes:

3. Explain why the increase in type 2 diabetes is considered epidemic in the developed world:

© BIOZONE International 2007
ISBN: 978-1-877462-13-9
Photocopying Prohibited

Related activities: The Control of Blood Glucose, Type 1 Diabetes

A 2

Substance Abuse

Drugs are substances that alter the functioning of the mind or body. Drug use is divided into medicinal treatments (used to treat a disease or its symptoms) and **recreational drugs** (used to enhance life experiences). Recreational drugs, e.g. marijuana, cocaine, metamphetamines, heroin, LSD, tranquillisers, and alcohol are usually taken for their mind-altering effects. Many recreational drugs are both psychologically and physically **addictive**. Once addicted, a user is unable to function without the drug. Moreover, because of the phenomenon of **drug tolerance**, ever-increasing doses are needed achieve the same effect. When the drug is withdrawn, they suffer **withdrawal** symptoms which can range from mild to life threatening.

1. Explain the difference between **psychological** addiction and **physical** addiction: _____

    _____

    _____

2. Outline the main effects of a **named** recreational drug: _____

    _____

    _____

3. Suggest how the use of recreational drugs by a pregnant woman would affect her unborn child: _____

    _____

    _____

© BIOZONE International 2007
ISBN: 978-1-877462-13-9
Photocopying Prohibited

RA 2   **Related activities**: Health vs Disease

Inherited Metabolic Disorders

Humans have more than 6000 physiological diseases attributed to mutations in single genes and over one hundred syndromes known to be caused by chromosomal abnormality. The number of genetic disorders identified increases every year. The work of the Human Genome Project is enabling the identification of the genetic basis of these disorders. This will facilitate the development of new drug therapies and gene therapies. Four genetic disorders are summarised below.

1. For each of the genetic disorder below, indicate the following:

   (a) Sickle cell disease: Gene name: __HBB__   Chromosome: _11_   Mutation type: _Substitution_____

   (b) β-thalassaemia: Gene name: _____   Chromosome: _____   Mutation type: _____

   (c) Cystic fibrosis: Gene name: _____   Chromosome: _____   Mutation type: _____

   (d) Huntington disease: Gene name: _____   Chromosome: _____   Mutation type: _____

2. Explain the cause of the symptoms for people suffering from β-thalassaemia: _____

   _____

3. Suggest a reason for the differences in the country-specific incidence rates for some genetic disorders: _____

   _____

   _____

A 2

The Fate of Conceptions

A significant number of conceptions do not end in live births. Even those that do may still have problems. A large proportion of miscarriages, which are spontaneous natural abortions, are caused by **chromosome disorders**: trisomy, polyploidy, and missing pieces of chromosomes. Some chromosome abnormalities are less severe than others and those affected survive into childhood or beyond. There is a strong correlation between the age of the mother and the incidence in chromosome abnormalities, called the **maternal age effect**. Prospective mothers older than 35-40 years of age are therefore encouraged to have a prenatal test (e.g. **amniocentesis** or **CVS**) to establish whether the fetus has a normal chromosome complement.

1. Discuss the role of the **maternal age effect** in the incidence rate of Down syndrome and other trisomic syndromes:

   _____

   _____

   _____

2. Explain the role of **amniocentesis** in detecting trisomic disorders: _____

   _____

   _____

3. Explain why, in recent times, most Down syndrome babies are born to younger mothers: _____

   _____

   _____

© BIOZONE International 2007
ISBN: 978-1-877462-13-9
Photocopying Prohibited

Related activities: Genetic Disorders

Genetic Disorders

Trisomy is a form of **aneuploidy** where the nucleus of the cells in an organism have one chromosome pair represented by three chromosomes (2N+1). The extra chromosome can grossly disturb the overall chromosomal balance resulting in abnormalities or death. In humans, about 50% of all spontaneous abortions result from chromosomal abnormalities, and trisomies are responsible for about half of these (25% of all spontaneous abortions). About 6% of live births result in children born with chromosomal abnormalities. Autosomal trisomies make up only 0.1% of all pregnancies. Of the three trisomics that survive to birth, **Down** syndrome (see below) is the most common. The other two trisomies, **Edward** and **Patau**, show severe mental and physical abnormalities (see below). Trisomy may be found in a few other autosomes, but they are extremely rare.

Related activities: The Fate of Conceptions

A 3

Non-Infectious Disease

1. (a) Study the three karyotype photographs (A-C) above and identify the three chromosomes (trisomy) that cause the syndromes listed below by placing a **circle** around them.

   (b) Identify each of the karyotypes (A-C) above, and state which chromosome is trisomic, and its incidence rate:

   Down syndrome: Karyotype: _____   Chromosome: _____   Incidence rate: _____

   Edward syndrome: Karyotype: _____   Chromosome: _____   Incidence rate: _____

   Patau syndrome: Karyotype: _____   Chromosome: _____   Incidence rate: _____

2. Describe the classic features of the phenotype of a Down syndrome person: _____

   _____

   _____

   _____

3. Explain why the presence of an extra chromosome has such a profound effect on the development of phenotype:

   _____

   _____

   _____

4. Describe the three main causes of Down syndrome and the percentage of cases arising for each:

   (a) Non-disjunction: _____

   _____

   (b) Translocation: _____

   _____

   (c) Mosaic: _____

   _____

© BIOZONE International 2007
ISBN: 978-1-877462-13-9
Photocopying Prohibited

Infectious Disease

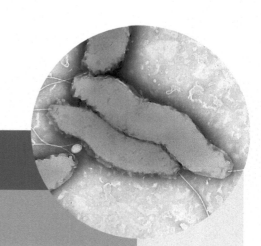

Investigating the nature of infectious disease: viral, bacterial, and fungal pathogens, parasites, and prions

Modes of transmission and vectors of disease, pathogens and their immunity to disease, case studies in human diseases.

Learning Objectives

☐ 1. Compile your own glossary from the **KEY WORDS** displayed in **bold type** in the learning objectives below.

The Nature of Disease *(pages 30, 55-59, 75-76)*

☐ 2. Define the terms **disease**, **infection**, **symptom**. Distinguish between **infectious disease** and non-infectious disease. Identify the role of **pathogens** in disease and list examples from different taxa.

☐ 3. Distinguish between a **pandemic** and an **epidemic**, and between **aetiology** and **epidemiology**. Identify the sort of information provided by epidemiological studies.

☐ 4. Recognise the contributions of **Robert Koch** and **Louis Pasteur** to the identification of microorganisms as the agents of disease. Outline **Koch's postulates** and explain how Koch's methodology helped to clarify the association between pathogens and disease.

☐ 5. Explain the modes of **transmission** for infectious diseases in populations. Explain the role of hygiene and sanitation in controlling some infectious diseases.

☐ 6. Distinguish between pathogens and **parasites** and between **endoparasites** and **ectoparasites**. Appreciate that some parasites can be **vectors** of disease, even if they do not cause it directly.

☐ 7. With respect to parasites, explain the terms: **primary host**, **secondary** (or intermediate) **host**. Using a named example, explain how parasitic stages are transmitted from host to host. Describe some of the adaptations of parasites that enable them to successfully locate a suitable host.

☐ 8. Describe the cause, transmission, effects, treatment, and control of at least one named infectious disease. You could choose from the case studies provided, or use an example of a locally occurring disease.

Viral Diseases *(pages 60-62, 95-98, 103)*

☐ 9. Describe the structural and functional features of human **viruses** and explain how different viral types are distinguished. Using a named example, describe how viral diseases are transmitted and how they infect a host and cause disease.

☐ 10. Explain the features of modern-day society that make widespread epidemics of virulent diseases more likely. Providing examples, explain the role of **vaccination** in the past and present control of viral diseases. Explain why it is difficult to develop vaccines against, or cures for, some viral diseases (e.g. HIV).

Case study: HIV/AIDS *(pages 63-66)*

☐ 11. Discuss the cause, transmission, and social implications of **HIV/AIDS**. Include reference to the role of social, economic, and biological factors in the distribution, spread, treatment, and control of AIDS.

☐ 12. Identify stages in the development of an HIV infection, including the effect of HIV on the immune system. Explain why AIDS is termed a **syndrome**.

☐ 13. Describe the probable origins of the two strains of HIV as cross species transfers (**zoonoses**).

Bacterial Disease *(pages 67-68, 95-97, 103)*

☐ 14. Identify the ways in which pathogenic bacteria cause disease. Giving examples, identify how bacterial diseases are transmitted. Relate the type and incidence of bacterial disease to the prevailing social conditions.

☐ 15. Describe factors affecting bacterial **pathogenicity**, including: features of the cell wall and capsule, **toxin** production, **infectivity**, and **invasiveness**. Distinguish between **exotoxins** (e.g *Staphylococcus*) and **endotoxins** (e.g. *Salmonella*). Recognise **enterotoxins** as exotoxins that affect the gastrointestinal tract.

☐ 16. With reference to **disinfectants**, **antiseptics**, and **antibiotics**, describe how bacterial diseases are controlled and treated.

Case study: tuberculosis (TB) *(page 69)*

☐ 17. Describe the causes and modes of transmission of TB. Assess the global importance of TB and understand its history in the human population, including reference to its **prevalence**, decline, and **reemergence**. Explain the importance of **carriers** in the spread of TB.

☐ 18. Discuss the treatment of TB, including the difficulties associated with increasing bacterial resistance to antibiotics. Describe the roles of social, economic, and biological factors in the control and prevention of TB.

Contamination of food & water *(pages 70, 95-96)*

☐ 19. Appreciate the role of inadequate provision of clean drinking water, poor sanitation, and/or poor food hygiene in the transmission of food and water-borne pathogens. Provide examples of food and waterborne diseases spread by the **faecal-oral route**.

☐ 20. Describe the causes and modes of transmission of **salmonellosis** and/or **staphylococcal food poisoning**. Describe factors governing the occurrence, prevention, and severity of these diseases.

Case study: cholera *(pages 71, 95)*

☐ 21. Describe the agent involved and modes of transmission of **cholera**. Assess the past and current global importance of cholera and relate its distribution to factors such as levels of sanitation and general poverty.

☐ 22. Discuss the roles of social, economic, and biological factors in controlling, preventing, and treating cholera.

Fungal Diseases *(pages 72, 97)*

☐ 23. Only a few fungi are pathogenic to humans and most of the diseases they cause tend to be **superficial diseases** of the skin and nails. Describe some of the fungal diseases affecting humans and identify the pathogen in each case.

☐ 24. Describe how fungi reproduce and infect a host and explain why fungal diseases tend to be **chronic** infections. Describe how fungal diseases are treated.

Multicellular Parasites *(pages 75-78)*

☐ 25. Describe a disease caused by a multicellular parasite, including reference the parasite's mode of transmission and life cycle. Examples could include: flatworms, e.g. **hydatid tapeworm** or *Schistosoma* or roundworms, e.g. *Ascaris* or hookworm.

☐ 26. Describe an example of an insect-carried infection of humans. Name some **ectoparasites** and the conditions or diseases for which they are responsible.

Protozoan Disease *(pages 73-74, 95-96)*

☐ 27. Describe the nature of **protozoan diseases**. Explain how some pathogenic **protozoans** are also parasites with part of their life cycle occurring in humans.

☐ 28. Identify the pathogen and mode of transmission of **malaria**. Assess malaria's global importance and identify biological factors in its distribution.

☐ 29. Describe the roles of social, economic, and biological factors in treating, controlling, and preventing malaria. Comment on the adequacy of these methods with reference to the difficulties associated with developing drugs against protozoans.

Emerging Diseases *(pages 79-82)*

☐ 30. Describe examples of **emerging diseases** and identify the threat that such diseases present to public health. Explain how emerging diseases may arise (e.g. through cross species transfer as a **zoonosis**).

☐ 31. Describe the nature of **prion diseases** and identify examples. Describe their mode of transmission, how they are thought to causes disease, the time period for development of symptoms, and the mortality.

☐ 32. Describe the agent involved and modes of transmission of a named emerging disease (other than HIV/AIDS). Identify the factors governing its emergence, global spread, and **virulence**, and explain how the pathogen was isolated and identified. Examples could include vCJD, Legionnaires' disease, SARS, or avian flu.

See page 7 for additional details of these texts:

■ Chenn, P. 1997. **Microorganisms and Biotechnology** (John Murray), Chpt 9 as required.

■ Clegg, C.J., 2002. **Microbes in Action**, (John Murray), chpt 1-5, 10 (treatment covered in context).

■ Freeland, P., 1999. **Microbes, Medicine and Commerce** (Hodder & Stoughton), chpt 2.

■ Fullick, A., 2000. **Human Health and Disease** (Heinemann), chpt 2.

■ Hudson, T. & K. Mannion, 2001. **Microbes and Disease** (Collins), chpt 4 and 5.

■ Murray, P. & N. Owens, 2001. **Behaviour and Populations** (Collins), chpt 6 and 7.

■ Taylor, J., 2001. **Microorganisms and Biotech-nology** (NelsonThornes), chpt 8.

See page 7 for details of publishers of periodicals:

STUDENT'S REFERENCE

■ **War on Disease** National Geographic 201(2) February 2002, pp. 4-31. *A great overview of the global importance of a range of infectious diseases.*

■ **Koch's Postulates** Biol. Sci. Rev., 15(3) February 2003, pp. 24-25. *Koch's postulates and the diagnosis of infectious disease.*

■ **Viral Plagues** Biol. Sci. Rev., 17(3) February 2005, pp. 37-41. *The nature of viruses and viral diseases, and what we can do to combat them.*

■ **The White Plague** New Scientist (Inside Science), 9 Nov. 2002. *The causes and nature of TB, the global incidence of TB, and the implications of increasing drug resistance to TB treatment.*

■ **Malaria** Biol. Sci. Rev., 15(1) Sept. 2002, pp. 29-33. *An account of the world's most important parasitic infection of humans. Symptoms, control and prevention, and future treatment options, as well as the parasite's life cycle, are discussed.*

■ **Tuberculosis** Biol. Sci. Rev., 14(1) Sept. 2001, pp. 30-33. *Despite vaccination, TB has become more common recently. Why has it returned?*

■ **Bedlam in the Blood** National Geographic, 212(1) 2007, pp. 32-67. *A comprehensive article*

on transmission and epidemiology of the malaria parasite, cure, prevention and vaccine strategies.

■ **Beating the Bloodsuckers** Biol. Sci. Rev., 16(3) Feb. 2004, pp. 31-35. *The nature and extent of malaria, including the biology of the Plasmodium parasite and the body's immune response to it.*

■ **Food / How Safe?** National Geographic, May 2002, pp. 2-31. *An excellent account of the issue of food safety and bacterial contamination of food.*

■ *Campylobacter ...*on the run Biol. Sci Rev., 19(3) Feb. 2007, pp. 7-9. *The physical characteristics of this bacterium.*

■ **Salmonella** Biol. Sci. Rev., 10(4) March 1998, pp.6-8. *Salmonella is an infectious bacterium which causes food poisoning and is a common contaminant of poultry and packaged foods.*

■ **No Mercy** New Scientist, 14 October 2000, pp. 28-32. *The flu virus: transmission and the spread of pandemics. This article also examines the role of animals as reservoirs for new flu strains.*

■ **Bacteria Can Count!** Biol. Sci. Rev., 13(2) November 2000, pp. 28-31. *The nature of bacteria and how they invade tissues and create infection.*

■ **Food / How Safe?** National Geographic, May 2002, pp. 2-31. *An excellent account of the issue of food safety and bacterial contamination of food.*

■ *Escherichia coli* O157 Biol. Sci. Rev., 10(3) Jan. 1998, pp. 9-11. *Transmission of disease by this virulent strain of E. coli. Covers symptoms, spread and control of the disease.*

■ **A Worm's Life** Biol. Sci. Rev.,13(5) May 2001, pp. 20-23. *Multicellular parasitic diseases and the threat they pose to human health (includes morphology and life cycle of a nematode worm).*

■ **Schistosomiasis** Biol. Sci. Rev., 16(3) Feb. 2004, pp. 21-25. *An account of the life cycle and reproductive biology of the schistosome fluke.*

■ **Fungi: Friends or Foes** Biol. Sci. Rev., 17(1) Sept. 2004, pp. 24-28. *The nature of fungi, their contributions in medicine and role as pathogens. Mycotoxins and the treatment of fungal diseases are also covered.*

■ **Search for a Cure** National Geographic 201(2) February 2002, pp. 32-43. *A current account of the global status of the AIDS epidemic, and an examination of the measures to stop it.*

■ **Opportunistic Infections and AIDS** Biol. Sci. Rev., 14 (4) April 2002, pp. 21-24. *An account of the suite of infections characterising AIDS (good).*

■ **Living with AIDS** National Geographic 208(3) Sept. 2005, pp. 66-73. *South Africans share their experiences of living with AIDS. This account includes a world map in which each country's size reflects the number of people with HIV/AIDS.*

■ **Rules of Contagion** New Scientist, 28 Oct. 2006, pp.44-47. *The levels of virulence of diseases.*

■ **Tracking the Next Flu Killer** National Geographic 208(4) Oct. 2005, pp. 4-31. *Avian flu compared with the 1918 Spanish flu and predictions of a possible bird flu pandemic.*

TEACHER'S REFERENCE

■ **We All Fall Down** New Scientist, 24 November 2001, pp. 34-37. *Everyone thinks that the Black Death was caused by bubonic plague, but some researchers believe the evidence available does not support this. Of interest to those interested in evidence for the origin and spread of a disease.*

■ **Positive Progress** New Scientist, 8 Feb. 2003, pp. 33-45. *A series of articles focusing on current issues in HIV research: why some individuals do not contract AIDS, the latest in vaccine development, and new measures against infection.*

■ **Is Global Warming Harmful to Health?** Scientific American, August 2000, pp. 36-43. *There is already evidence that a warming climate will promote the spread of infectious disease.*

■ **New Medicines for the Developing World** Biol. Sci. Rev. 14 (1) Sept. 2001, pp. 22-26. *The politics of treating disease in the developing world: why is there little incentive to develop programmes to prevent and treat some diseases?*

See pages 4-5 for details of how to access **Bio Links** from our web site: **www.thebiozone.com** From Bio Links, access sites under the topics:

HEALTH & DISEASE: • CDC disease links • CDC: Avian influenza • WHO/OMS: health topics > **Infectious Diseases:** • Centers for Disease Control and Prevention (CDC) • Cholera and epidemic dysentery • Disease-causing bacteria • Emerging infectious diseases • HIV Insite: gateway to AIDS knowledge • Koch's postulates • Meningococcal disease • Prion diseases • Public Health Laboratory Service: Disease facts • Insect vectors of human pathogens • SARS (from WHO) • Coronaviruses • SARS quarantine... *and others*

Presentation MEDIA to support this topic:

HEALTH & DISEASE:
• **The Nature of Disease**
• **Infectious Disease**

Infection and Disease

Infectious disease refers to disease caused by a **pathogen** (an infectious agent). In 1861, **Louis Pasteur** demonstrated experimentally that microorganisms can be present in non-living matter and can contaminate seemingly sterile solutions. He also showed conclusively that microbes can be destroyed by heat; a discovery that formed the basis of modern-day **aseptic** **technique**. The development of the germ theory of disease followed Pasteur's discoveries and, in 1876-1877, **Robert Koch** established a sequence of experimental steps (known as **Koch's postulates**) for directly relating a specific microbe to a specific disease. During the past 100 years, the postulates have been invaluable in determining the specific agents of many diseases.

1. Using a named example, explain what is meant by a **pathogen**: _____

_____

2. Explain the contribution of Robert Koch to the **aetiology** of disease: _____

_____

_____

_____

3. Suggest why diseases caused by **intracellular protozoan parasites** can be particularly difficult to control and treat:

_____

_____

_____

Infectious Disease

Related activities: Patterns of Disease

RA 2

The Role of Health Statistics

Health is difficult to define and to measure, and most of the information about the state of health of a nation's population comes from studying disease. **Epidemiology** is the study of the occurrence and the spread of disease. The **health statistics** collected by epidemiologists are used by health authorities to identify patterns of disease in their country. These patterns, including the **incidence** and **prevalence** of a disease are important in planning health services and investigating causes of disease. Health statistics enable the effectiveness of health policies and practices, such as vaccination programmes, to be monitored. The World Health Organisation (WHO) gathers data on an international basis to identify global patterns.

1. Explain the contribution of epidemiologists to monitoring public health: _____

_____

2. Describe the trend in BMI between 1993 and 1999 (Figure 1): _____

_____

3. (a) Suggest a probable reason for the pattern of reported cases of *Haemophilus influenzae* (Figure 3) prior to 1993:

_____

(b) Suggest a possible cause for the decline in the incidence of *Haemophilius influenzae* after 1993: _____

_____

4. (a) Identify a difference between the cause of death between developed and developing countries: _____

_____

(b) Explain this difference: _____

© BIOZONE International 2007
ISBN: 978-1-877462-13-9
Photocopying Prohibited

RA 2   **Related activities**: Patterns of Disease, Epidemiology of AIDS, Immunisation

Patterns of Disease

Diseases present in low levels of a population at any time are known as **endemic** diseases. Occasionally there may be a sudden increase in the **prevalence** of a particular disease. On a local level this is known as an **outbreak**. Such an increase in prevalence on a national scale is called an **epidemic**. An epidemic occurs when an infectious disease spreads rapidly through a population and affects large numbers of people. One example is influenza, epidemics of which are relatively common and occur every two to three years. On rare occasions an epidemic disease will spread to other countries throughout the world. This is known as a **pandemic**. Examples

of diseases that are known to have caused pandemics are bubonic plague, cholera, tuberculosis, HIV/AIDS, and influenza. **Epidemiologists** gather data on the number of infected people (**morbidity**) and the number of people that have died (**mortality**) within a population. These data help to establish the **incidence** (number of new cases per unit time) and **prevalence** (number of infected people expressed as a proportion of the population) of the disease in the population at any given time. **Aetiology** is the study of the cause of a disease. It can assist in pinpointing the origin of new diseases, such as the respiratory disease SARS, as they arise in populations.

1. Using examples, distinguish between different patterns of disease (epidemic, pandemic, and endemic disease):

_____

_____

_____

_____

_____

2. Suggest why it is important to establish the **incidence** of a disease when it begins to spread through a community:

_____

_____

Infectious Disease

Related activities: The Role of Health Statistics, Cholera, Epidemiology of AIDS, The Control of Disease

A 2

3. Severe Acute Respiratory Disease (SARS) is a serious respiratory disease, which appeared in the human population in 2003 and spread rapidly through coughing and sneezing. Its epidemiology provides a good example of how health authorities can work together to locate the origin of a disease and halt its spread:

(a) Describe the pattern of spread of SARS in Toronto, Canada: _____

_____

(b) Describe the particular features of disease control that were important in containing the spread of SARS:

_____

_____

(c) Identify which aspect of modern life contributed to the rapid global spread of SARS: _____

_____

_____

4. Suggest why aetiology is important when controlling an outbreak of a new disease: _____

_____

_____

ISBN: 978-1-877462-13-9

Transmission of Disease

The human body is no different to that of other large animals in that it is under constant attack by a wide range of organisms wanting to penetrate its defences. Once inside us, these organisms will seek to reproduce and exploit us for food. Some of these organisms may be pathogens. Pathogens may be transferred from one individual to another by a number of methods (below). The transmission of infectious diseases can be virtually eliminated by observing appropriate personal hygiene procedures, providing adequate sanitation, and chlorinating drinking water.

1. Describe three personal hygiene practices that would minimise the risk of transmitting an infectious disease:

   (a) _____

   (b) _____

   (c) _____

2. Identify the common **mode of transmission** and the **portal of entry** for the following pathogens:

   (a) Protozoan causing malaria: _____

   (b) Tetanus bacteria: _____

   (c) Cholera bacteria: _____

   (d) Common cold virus: _____

   (e) Tuberculosis bacteria: _____

   (f) HIV (AIDS) virus: _____

   (g) Gonorrhoea bacteria: _____

Infectious Disease

Related activities: Bacterial Diseases, Tuberculosis, Cholera, Viral Diseases, HIV and AIDS, The Control of Disease

RA 2

The Structure of Viruses

Viruses are non-cellular **obligate intracellular parasites**, requiring a living host cell in order to reproduce. A typical, fully developed viral particle (**virion**) lacks the metabolic machinery of cells, containing just a single type of nucleic acid (DNA or RNA) encased in a protein coat or **capsid**. Being non-cellular, viruses do not conform to the existing criteria upon which a five or six kingdom classification system is based. Viruses can be distinguished by their structure (see below) and by the nature of their genetic material (single or double stranded DNA or RNA).

Those that use bacterial cells as a host (called **bacteriophages**) can be grown on bacterial cultures, but other viruses, such as those affecting humans are more difficult to study because they require living animals, embryos, or cell cultures in order to replicate. The particular **host range** of a virus is determined by the virus's requirements for attaching to the host cell and the availability, within the host, of the cellular factors needed for viral multiplication. For animal viruses, the receptor sites are on the plasma membranes of the host cells.

Types of Viruses Affecting Humans

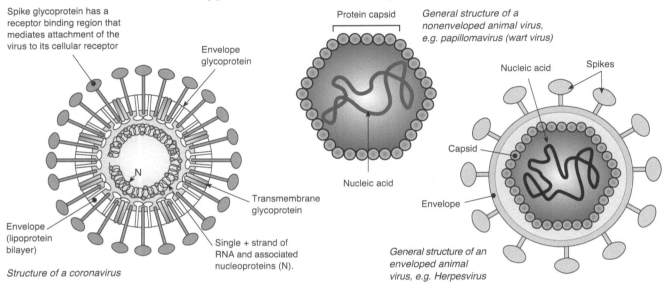

Spike glycoprotein has a receptor binding region that mediates attachment of the virus to its cellular receptor

Envelope glycoprotein

Transmembrane glycoprotein

Envelope (lipoprotein bilayer)

Single + strand of RNA and associated nucleoproteins (N).

N

Structure of a coronavirus

Protein capsid

General structure of a nonenveloped animal virus, e.g. papillomavirus (wart virus)

Nucleic acid

Nucleic acid

Spikes

Capsid

Envelope

General structure of an enveloped animal virus, e.g. Herpesvirus

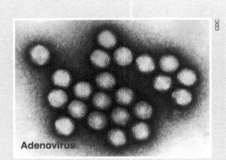

Adenovirus

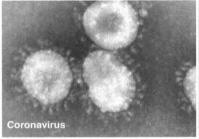

Coronavirus

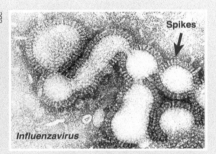

Spikes

Influenzavirus

Adenoviruses are medium-sized (90-100 nm), nonenveloped viruses containing double-stranded DNA. They most commonly cause respiratory illness and are unusually stable to chemical or physical agents, allowing for prolonged survival outside of the body.

Coronaviruses primarily infect the upper respiratory and gastrointestinal tracts of birds and mammals, including humans. Their name derives from the crown or corona of spikes and they have the largest genome of any of the single stranded RNA viruses.

In some viruses, the capsid is covered by an **envelope**, which protects the virus from the host's nuclease enzymes. Spikes on the envelope provide a binding site for attachment to the host. **Influenzavirus** is an enveloped virus with many glycoprotein spikes.

1. Describe the basis of viral host specificity and explain why viruses generally show a very narrow host range:

   _____

   _____

2. In view of your answer above, explain why it is not uncommon for viruses to cross the species barrier to infect another host type. Provide an example to illustrate your answer:

   _____

   _____

   _____

© BIOZONE International 2007
ISBN: 978-1-877462-13-9

Viral Diseases

Viruses are found as intracellular parasites in all kinds of organisms, and they are responsible for a number of crop and livestock diseases and many diseases of humans. Antiviral drugs are difficult to design because they must kill the virus without killing the host cells. Moreover, viruses cannot be attacked when in an inert state. Antiviral drugs work by preventing entry of the virus into the host cell or by interfering with their replication. There are only a few antiviral drugs currently in use (e.g. ribavirin to combat influenza, acyclovir to combat herpes, AZT and protease inhibitors to combat HIV/AIDS). Immunisation is still regarded as the most effective way in which to control viral disease. However immunisation against viruses does not necessarily provide lifelong immunity. New strains of viruses develop as preexisting strains acquire mutations. These mutations allow the viruses to change their surface proteins and thus evade immediate immune system detection.

1. Summarize important features of each of the following viral pathogens. For disease symptoms, consult a textbook, the internet, a good dictionary, or an encyclopedia:

(a) HIV causes the disease: _____

   Natural reservoir: _____ Symptoms: _____

   _____

   _____

(b) Coronaviruses cause: _____

   Natural reservoir: _____ Symptoms: _____

   _____

   _____

(c) *Influenzavirus* causes the disease: _____

   Natural reservoir: _____ Symptoms: _____

   _____

   _____

Infectious Disease

Related activities: The Structure of Viruses, HIV and AIDS

RA 2

2. State the purpose of the glycoprotein spikes found on some enveloped viruses: _____

_____

3. (a) Explain the significance of endocytosis to the entry of an enveloped virus into an animal cell: _____

_____

(b) State where an enveloped virus replicates its viral DNA: _____

(c) State where an enveloped virus synthesises its proteins: _____

4. Summarise the steps involved in invasion of a host cell by an enveloped viral particle such as *Influenzavirus*:

(a) Attachment: _____

_____

(b) Penetration: _____

_____

(c) Uncoating: _____

_____

5. Giving an example, explain why it is difficult to develop suitable long term vaccines against some viruses: _____

_____

_____

6. Explain how viruses may cause some forms of cancer: _____

_____

_____

7. Describe two ways in which viruses can cause disease:

(a) _____

(b) _____

© BIOZONE International 2007
ISBN: 978-1-877462-13-9
Photocopying Prohibited

HIV and AIDS

AIDS (acquired immune deficiency syndrome) first appeared in the news in 1981, with cases being reported in Los Angeles, in the United States. By 1983, the pathogen causing the disease had been identified as a retrovirus that selectively infects **helper T cells**. The disease causes a massive deficiency in the immune system due to infection with **HIV** (human immunodeficiency virus). HIV is a retrovirus (RNA, not DNA) and is able to splice its genes into the host cell's chromosome. As yet, there is no cure or vaccine, and the disease has taken the form of a **pandemic**, spreading to all parts of the globe and killing more than a million people each year. It has now been established that HIV arose by the recombination of two simian viruses. It has probably been endemic in some central African regions for decades, as HIV has been found in blood samples from several African nations from as early as 1959. HIV's mode of infection is described overleaf and its origin and prevalence are covered in the next activity.

1. Explain what is meant by **HIV positive**: _____

   _____

2. Consult the graph above showing the stages of HIV infection (remember, HIV infects and destroys helper T cells).

   (a) Describe how the virus population changes with the progression of the disease: _____

   _____

   _____

   (b) Describe how the helper T cells respond to the infection: _____

   _____

Infectious Disease

Related activities: Epidemiology of AIDS, Resistance in Pathogens

DA 2

3. Explain why the HIV virus has such a devastating effect on our body's ability to fight disease: _____

_____

_____

4. (a) Explain the role of the reverse transcriptase in the life cycle of a retrovirus such as HIV: _____

_____

_____

(b) Explain the significance of the formation of a provirus: _____

_____

5. Identify three ways in which HIV is commonly transmitted from one person to another: _____

_____

6. In the years immediately following the discovery of the HIV pathogen, there was a sudden appearance of AIDS cases amongst **haemophiliacs** (people with an inherited blood disorder). State why this group was being infected with HIV:

_____

_____

7. Explain why it has been so difficult to develop a **vaccine** against HIV: _____

_____

_____

8. In a rare number of cases, people who have been HIV positive for many years still have no apparent symptoms. Explain the significance of this observation and its likely potential in the search for a cure for AIDS:

_____

_____

© BIOZONE International 2007
ISBN: 978-1-877462-13-9
Photocopying Prohibited

Epidemiology of AIDS

In many urban centers of sub-Saharan Africa, Latin America, and the Caribbean, AIDS has already become the leading cause of death for both men and women aged 15 to 49 years. AIDS kills people in their most productive years and ranks as the leading cause of potential healthy life-years lost in sub-Saharan Africa. Within the next decade, crude death rates in some countries will more than double, and infant and child mortality rates will increase markedly. Perhaps the most significant impact will be seen in projected life expectancies due to the increased mortality of young adults. The AIDS pandemic has lowered the estimated world population level for the year 2050 from 9.4 billion to 8.9 billion – mostly caused by the massive toll of AIDS in Africa.

Infectious Disease

© BIOZONE International 2007
ISBN: 978-1-877462-13-9
Photocopying Prohibited

Related activities: HIV and AIDS, The Control of Disease

DA 2

1. Discuss the social, economic, and biological factors involved in the prevalence of HIV in many of the **rural** communities of sub-Saharan Africa:

_____

_____

_____

_____

_____

2. Describe the effects of AIDS on the countries of sub-Saharan Africa with respect to the following:

   (a) Age structure of their populations: _____

   _____

   (b) Their local economies: _____

   _____

3. Effective antiviral therapies have reduced deaths from HIV/AIDS in developed countries. Explain why a similar reduction has not occurred in the countries of sub-Saharan Africa:

_____

_____

4. Briefly describe the origin of the two main strains of HIV:

   HIV-1: _____

   _____

   HIV-2: _____

   _____

5. Using the information provided on the opposite page and your own graph paper, plot a column graph of the number of people living with HIV/AIDS for each region. Staple the completed graph into this workbook.

© BIOZONE International 2007
ISBN: 978-1-877462-13-9
Photocopying Prohibited

Bacterial Diseases

Of the many species of bacteria that exist in the world, relatively few cause disease in humans. The diagram below shows four adaptive features that help bacteria infect host tissue and cause disease. Bacteria infect a host to exploit the food potential of its body tissues. The fact that this exploitation causes disease is not in the interest of the bacteria; a healthy host is better than a sick one. Some human diseases caused by bacteria are illustrated in the diagram below. The natural reservoir (source of infection) of a disease varies from species to species, ranging from humans, insects, and other animals, to sewage and contaminated water.

Related activities: Cholera, Foodborne Disease, The Control of Disease

RA 2

Infectious Disease

1. Explain the importance of determining the natural reservoir of infection when attempting to control a bacterial disease:

_____

_____

_____

2. Distinguish between exotoxins and endotoxins, identifying the role of each in disease: _____

_____

_____

_____

_____

3. Summarise important features of each of the following bacterial pathogens. For disease symptoms, consult a textbook, the internet, a good dictionary, or an encyclopedia:

   (a) *Salmonella* bacteria cause the disease: _____

   Natural reservoir: _____ Symptoms: _____

   _____

   (b) *Clostridium botulinum* causes the disease: _____

   Natural reservoir: _____ Symptoms: _____

   _____

   (c) *Staphylococcus aureus* causes the disease: _____

   Natural reservoir: _____ Symptoms: _____

   _____

4. Describe three common features of the three bacterial pathogens identified in the previous question:

   (a) _____

   (b) _____

   (c) _____

Tuberculosis

Tuberculosis (TB) is a contagious disease caused by the *Mycobacterium tuberculosis* bacterium (**MTB**). The breakdown in health services in some countries, the spread of HIV/AIDS, and the emergence of **multidrug-resistant TB** are contributing to the increasingly harmful impact of this disease. In 1993, the World Health Organisation (WHO) responded to the growing pandemic and declared TB a global emergency. By 1998, the WHO estimated that about a third of the world's population were already infected with MTB. They estimate that 8 million new cases are added annually and that TB causes about 2 million deaths each year (note that in the figures given below, only *notified cases* are reported). If controls are not strengthened, it is anticipated that between 2002 and 2020, approximately 1000 million people will be newly infected, over 150 million people will get sick, and 36 million will die from TB.

1. Identify the pathogen that causes tuberculosis (TB): _____

2. Explain how MTB may exist in a dormant state in a person for many years without causing disease symptoms:

   _____

   _____

3. State how TB is transmitted between people: _____

   _____

4. Suggest how some strains of MTB have acquired **multi-drug resistance**: _____

   _____

   _____

Infectious Disease

Related activities: Resistance in Pathogens, Antibiotic Resistance

A 2

Foodborne Disease

Foodborne disease is caused by consuming contaminated foods or beverages. More than 250 food and waterborne diseases have been identified. The symptoms and severity of these vary according to the infectious agent, although diarrhoea and vomiting are two universal symptoms. Food poisoning is a term used for any gastrointestinal illness with sudden onset, usually accompanied by stomach pain, diarrhoea, and vomiting, and caused by eating **contaminated food**. It is a common cause of **gastroenteritis**. Food and waterborne diseases cause an estimated 76 million illnesses annually in the USA alone, although as many as 20% of these are probably acquired abroad. Such illnesses usually result from food contaminated with viruses, or bacteria or their toxins. They may also result from contamination of food or water by chemicals such as nitrates.

1. Describe three ways in which food can become contaminated by *E. coli*: _____

_____

_____

2. Describe why food poisoning is more prevalent in developing countries: _____

_____

_____

3. Outline the basic precautions that should be taken with drinking water when travelling to developing countries:

_____

_____

4. (a) Describe the symptoms of salmonellosis: _____

_____

(b) Identify the method of transmission of this disease: _____

5. Explain why reheating food will still cause food poisoning if the food is contaminated with *Staphylococcus aureus*:

_____

© BIOZONE International 2007
ISBN: 978-1-877462-13-9
Photocopying Prohibited

Cholera

Cholera is an acute intestinal infection caused by the bacterium *Vibrio cholerae*. The disease has a short incubation period, from one to five days. The bacterium produces an enterotoxin that causes a copious, painless, watery diarrhoea that can quickly lead to severe dehydration and death if treatment is not promptly given. Most people infected with *V. cholerae* do not become ill, although the bacterium is present in their faeces for 7-14 days. When cholera appears in a community it is essential to take measures against its spread. These include: **hygienic disposal of human faeces**, provision of an adequate supply of **safe drinking water**, **safe food handling and preparation** (e.g. preventing contamination of food and cooking food thoroughly), and **effective general hygiene** (e.g. hand washing with soap). Cholera has reemerged as a global health threat after virtually disappearing from the Americas and most of Africa and Europe for more than a century. Originally restricted to the Indian subcontinent, cholera spread to Europe in 1817 in the first of seven pandemics. The current pandemic (below) shows signs of slowly abating, although under-reporting is a problem.

1. Identify the pathogen that causes cholera: _____

2. (a) Describe the symptoms of cholera: _____
   _____

   (b) Explain why these symptoms are so dangerous if not treated quickly: _____
   _____

3. State how cholera is transmitted between people: _____
   _____

4. Describe the effective treatment of cholera at the following stages in the progression of the disease:

   (a) Mild onset of dehydration: _____

   (b) Severe symptoms: _____

5. Identify the risk factors associated with the incidence of cholera and relate these to social and economic conditions:
   _____
   _____
   _____

Infectious Disease

Related activities: Bacterial Diseases, Transmission of Disease, Patterns of Disease, The Control of Disease

A 2

Fungal Diseases

The study of fungi (moulds, yeasts, and fleshy fungi) is called **mycology**. All fungi are chemoheterotrophs, requiring organic compounds for energy and carbon. Most fungi are saprophytes, and are found in the soil and water, where they decompose organic matter using extracellular enzymes. Of the 100 000 species of fungi, only about 100 species are pathogenic to humans and other animals, although thousands of fungal species are pathogenic to plants. Any fungal infection is called a **mycosis**. They are generally **chronic** (long-lasting) infections because fungi grow relatively slowly. Fungal infections are divided into three groups according to the degree of tissue involvement and the mode of entry into the host. Characteristics of these groups are summarised in the diagram below. Some of these infections (e.g. candidiasis) can also be classed opportunistic, because they occur when the host is immune depressed or weakened in some way.

1. Distinguish between cutaneous and subcutaneous fungal infections, identifying why subcutaneous infections are rarer:

   _____

   _____

2. Suggest which individuals would be at greatest risk from systemic fungal infections and why: _____

   _____

   _____

3. Explain why fungal infections tend to be **chronic**: _____

   _____

4. Suggest how the spread of athlete's foot (*Tinea pedis*) can be limited by thorough drying of the feet: _____

   _____

Protozoan Diseases

Protozoa are one-celled, eukaryotic organisms that belong to the Kingdom Protista (Protoctista). Among the protozoans, there are many variations on cell structure. While most inhabit water and soil habitats, some are part of the natural microbiota of animals (i.e. they are microorganisms that live on or in animals). Relatively few of the nearly 20 000 species of protozoans cause disease; those that do are often highly specialised, intracellular parasites with complex life cycles involving one or more hosts. Under certain adverse conditions, some protozoans produce a protective capsule called a **cyst**. A cyst allows the protozoan to survive conditions unsuitable for survival. For specialised parasitic species, this includes survival for periods outside a host.

1. Some protozoans form cysts under certain conditions.

   (a) Explain what a **cyst** is: _____

   _____

   (b) Explain how the ability to form a cyst helps a parasitic protozoan to survive: _____

   _____

   _____

2. Several parasitic protozoans causing diseases in humans use other animal species as hosts for part of their life cycle. Identify the host (including class and genus) that is involved in part of the life cycle for each of the following diseases:

   (a) Sleeping sickness: _____

   (b) Malaria: _____

3. The disease known as **giardia** is an increasingly common problem for campers. In seemingly remote areas, campers may contract this disease by drinking water from streams and lakes. Briefly explain the likely reason for this:

   _____

4. Describe the likely conditions under which amoebic dysentery is transmitted: _____

   _____

© BIOZONE International 2007
ISBN: 978-1-877462-13-9
Photocopying Prohibited

Infectious Disease

Malaria

Malaria is a serious parasitic disease, spread by bites of **Anopheles** mosquitoes, affecting up to 300 million people in the tropics each year. The parasites responsible for malaria are protozoa known as **plasmodia**. Four species can cause the disease in humans. Each spends part of its life cycle in humans and part in *Anopheles* mosquitoes. Even people who take antimalarial drugs and precautions against being bitten may contract malaria. Malaria, especially *falciparum* malaria, is often a medical emergency that requires hospitalisation. Treatment involves the use of antimalarial drugs and, in severe cases, blood transfusions may be necessary. Symptoms, which appear one to two weeks after being bitten, include headache, shaking, chills, and fever. *Falciparum* malaria is more severe, with high fever, coma, and convulsions, and it can be fatal within a few days of the first symptoms. These more severe symptoms result from this plasmodium's ability to infect all ages of red blood cells (whereas other species attack only young or old cells). Destruction of a greater proportion of blood cells results in *haemolytic anaemia*. The infected blood cells become sticky and block blood vessels to vital organs such as the kidneys and the brain.

1. Explain how a *Plasmodium* parasite enters the body: _____

   _____

2. Suggest a way in which villagers could reduce the occurrence of malaria carrying mosquitoes in their immediate area:

   _____

3. (a) Describe the symptoms of a malaria attack: _____

   _____

   (b) Explain why the symptoms of *falciparum* malaria are more severe than other forms of malaria: _____

   _____

   _____

4. Global warming is expected to increase the geographical area of malaria infection. Explain why this is expected:

   _____

   _____

Related activities: Protozoan Diseases, Resistance in Pathogens

Multicellular Parasites

Multicellular parasites comprise more than a single cell and are relatively complex organisms. Some **endoparasites**, such as flatworms and roundworms, cause disease directly and are highly specialised to live inside their hosts. Parasitic forms differ from their free-living relatives in the following ways: they have no digestive system or one that is highly simplified, their nervous system is reduced, they have little or no means of locomotion, and their reproductive system is often complex, with an individual producing large numbers of fertilised eggs to infect a new host. Some insects and arachnids (especially ticks and mites), apart from being **ectoparasites**, can also carry disease-causing microorganisms between hosts. They act as **vectors**, picking up bacteria, viruses, or protozoans when they suck the blood of their host. Some vectors are just a mechanical means of transport for a pathogen. Other parasites multiply in their vectors and can accumulate in the vector's saliva or faeces.

1. (a) Distinguish between endoparasites and ectoparasites: _____

    _____

   (b) State which of these are most likely to be vectors of disease rather than pathogens themselves and explain why:

    _____

    _____

2. Suggest why many of the diseases carried by insect vectors are restricted to tropical regions: _____

    _____

    _____

3. Trichinosis is spread by the ingestion of undercooked meat (e.g. pork) infected with the parasite. Explain why a human infection of trichinosis is a dead end for the parasite:

    _____

    _____

Infectious Disease

Related activities: Infection and Disease, The Schistosoma Parasite, Hookworm Infection

RA 3

4. Explain why tapeworms, as a result of their parasitic way of life, have the following special features:

(a) No digestive system: _____

_____

_____

(b) No means of locomotion: _____

_____

_____

(c) Reduced nervous system: _____

_____

_____

5. Draw a diagram to summarise the life cycle of the parasite **hydatid tapeworm**:

The Schistosoma Parasite

Some **endoparasites**, such as flatworms and roundworms, cause disease directly and are highly specialised to live inside their hosts. Schistosomes, or blood flukes, are specialised parasitic **trematode flatworms** of the genus *Schistosoma*. They are found as adults in the blood vessels of their mammalian hosts and cause the disease **schistosomiasis**, one of the most widespread and devastating parasitic diseases of humans. It is endemic in 74 developing countries with more than 80% of infected people living in sub-Saharan Africa. Unlike most other flukes, schistosomes have separate sexes, and the female and male remain clasped together for their entire reproductive life. Transmission of the *Schistosoma* parasite occurs in freshwater when intermediate snail hosts release infective larval forms of the parasite (cercariae). In intestinal schistosomiasis, there is progressive enlargement of the spleen and liver, and intestinal damage and bleeding. The disease has a low fatality rate, but a high morbidity. Sufferers become severely weakened and liver, spleen, and kidney function become impaired.

1. Outline the features of each stage of the *Schistosoma* life cycle, including the important adaptive features of each stage:

   (a) Egg: _____

   _____

   (b) Miracidium larva: _____

   _____

   (c) Cercariae larva: _____

   _____

   (d) Adult fluke: _____

   _____

2. Describe biological and social factors that might be influential in the **prevalence** of intestinal schistosomiasis:

   _____

   _____

Infectious Disease

Related activities: Multicellular Parasites

RA 3

Hookworm Infection

Hookworm infestations affect about 700 million people worldwide, mainly those living in the tropics, and were once very common in the south-western states of the USA. With improved sanitation, its incidence has declined greatly. There are two species of hookworm: *Ancylostoma duodenale* and *Necator americanus*. Collectively they perform the equivalent of draining the blood from some 1.5 million people every day. Antihelminthic drugs, such as mebendazole, kill the worms but only effective sanitation can eliminate the disease. The diagram below illustrates the life cycle and distribution of *Necator americanus*.

1. Explain how a hookworm enters the body: _____

   _____

2. Suggest a simple precaution that could severely reduce hookworm infestations: _____

   _____

3. Describe the symptoms of a hookworm infection: _____

   _____

4. Explain why these symptoms are produced by a hookworm infection: _____

   _____

   _____

5. Name the role of humans in the life cycle of hookworms: _____

© BIOZONE International 2007
ISBN: 978-1-877462-13-9
Photocopying Prohibited

Prion Diseases

Until recently, all pathogens were thought to contain some form of nucleic acid. It now seems possible that a protein alone can be an infectious agent. Called **prions**, they are capable of replication and of causing infection. Prions have been spread by eating contaminated meat and, because they resist normal sterilisation methods, they can be spread on surgical instruments. Prions are produced by mutations in the gene coding for a normal cell protein (PrP). They cause a group of degenerative nervous diseases in mammals called transmissible spongiform encephalopathies (TSE). These include scrapie in sheep, bovine spongiform encephalopathy (**BSE**) in cattle, and variant **Creutzfeldt-Jakob disease** and **kuru** in humans. Different mutations of the PrP gene are thought to be responsible in each case.

Infectious Disease

Related activities: Emerging Diseases, The Control of Disease

DA 2

1. Describe the main feature of prions that distinguishes them from other infectious agents: _____

_____

2. Explain briefly how a prion is able to replicate inside a mammal's body: _____

_____

_____

_____

3. In 1988, the British government introduced a ban on feeding cattle with meat and bone meal.

   (a) Explain the purpose of this ban: _____

   _____

   (b) Suggest why the incidence of **BSE** continued to increase for a number of years after the ban: _____

   _____

   _____

4. State the source of infection for people with **variant CJD**: _____

5. Describe the cultural practice of highland tribes of Papua New Guinea that spread the prion disease known as **kuru**:

   _____

   _____

6. Name a prion disease that affects the following mammals:

   (a) Sheep: _____ (b) Cattle: _____ (c) Humans: _____

7. Identify three medical procedures that have been known to accidentally introduce CJD into patients: _____

   _____

Emerging Diseases

Emerging diseases are so named because they are diseases with no previous history in the human population. Often, as with HIV/AIDS and avian influenza (H5N1), they are **zoonoses** (animal diseases that cross to humans). Zoonoses are capable of causing highly lethal **pandemics** (world-wide epidemics) amongst an unprepared population. The increasing incidence of **multiple drug resistance** in pathogens (including those that cause tuberculosis, malaria, pneumonia, gonorrhoea, and cholera) has lead to the **re-emergence** of diseases that were previously thought to be largely under control. Food-borne diseases, such as *Campylobacter*, are also on the rise, despite improvements in hygiene. Even diseases once thought to be non-infectious (e.g. stomach ulcers and cervical cancer) are now known to be linked to infectious agents. In the 1940s, many common and lethal diseases (e.g. scarlet fever and diphtheria) were conquered using antibiotics. It is now evident that antibiotics are not only losing their power, they are encouraging the emergence of deadly and untreatable infections.

Infectious Disease

Related activities: Patterns of Disease, HIV and AIDS, Prion Diseases,
Resistance in Pathogens

RA 2

1. Describe the biological and social factors important in the emergence and spread of a named **emerging disease**:

   _____

   _____

   _____

   _____

   _____

   _____

2. Explain the role of **zoonoses** in the emergence of new diseases: _____

   _____

   _____

3. Using an example, explain what a **re-emerging disease** is: _____

   _____

   _____

4. Explain how drug resistance in pathogens has led to an increase in the number of re-emerging diseases:

   _____

   _____

   _____

5. Describe the biological and social factors involved when diseases spread rapidly through hospitals:

   _____

   _____

   _____

6. The Spanish influenza pandemic of 1917-18 was made worse by the return of troops from World War I to their home countries. More than 20 million people died in the pandemic, which had a death rate of about 3%. Explain how this pandemic differed from that of SARS in 2003, in terms of its **global spread** and **death rate**:

   _____

   _____

   _____

7. The next pandemic may well be avian flu. Discuss why this disease poses such a public health threat and describe the precautions necessary in preventing its global spread:

   _____

   _____

   _____

   _____

8. Haemorrhagic fevers are frightening diseases because of their sudden onset, distressing symptoms, and high fatality. Suggest why, although virulent, they pose less risk of a pandemic than influenza:

   _____

   _____

   _____

   _____

Preventing and Treating Disease

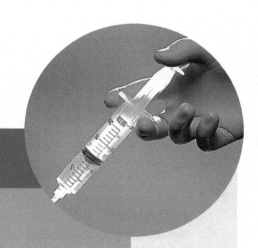

Diagnosing, treating, and preventing disease

Public health and quarantine. Vaccines and immunisation. Preventing lifestyle disease. Methods for diagnosing and treating disease.

Learning Objectives

☐ 1. Compile your own glossary from the **KEY WORDS** displayed in **bold type** in the learning objectives below.

Public Health & Quarantine *(pages 56-59, 95-96)*

☐ 2. Explain the importance of disease prevention to public health. Identify the role of (improved) **hygiene** and **sanitation** in controlling some infectious diseases. Discuss why disease prevention is more difficult where hygiene standards are poor and there is inadequate clean water.

☐ 3. Explain what is meant by **quarantine**. Explain the important role of quarantine measures in preventing the spread of disease between countries.

☐ 4. Distinguish between **antiseptics** and **disinfectants** and state their role in preventing the spread of disease. Explain the role of pesticides in controlling vector borne diseases (particularly in tropical countries).

☐ 5. Explain what is meant by a **public health programme**. Explain the role of such programmes in preventing disease. Outline the reliance of such programmes on public education and the availability of suitable facilities.

☐ 6. Explain the purpose of **health statistics** and describe the sort of information that they provide. Explain the role of health statistics in public health programmes.

Preventing Lifestyle Diseases *(pages 91-94)*

☐ 7. Discuss the role of diet, exercise, and stress relief in the prevention of some lifestyle diseases (e.g. obesity).

☐ 8. Explain what is meant by a **balanced diet** recognising the role of each of the following: proteins, fats, carbohydrates, vitamins, and minerals.

☐ 9. Discuss the energy and nutrient requirements of people with reference to gender, age, level of activity, pregnancy, and lactation. Describe the role of **Recommended Dietary Intakes** and their equivalents (e.g. **Recommended Daily Amounts** and **Dietary Reference Values**) in determining nutritional guidelines. Recognise that these values are country specific and are not necessarily always based on the same criteria.

Vaccines & Immunisation *(pages 23, 103-108)*

☐ 10. Review the distinction between passive and **active immunity**. Define the terms: **vaccine**, **immunity**, **vaccination** (= **immunisation**). Appreciate that **immunisation** involves the production of immunity by artificial means and that **vaccination** usually refers to immunisation by inoculation. Know that these terms are frequently used synonymously.

☐ 11. Explain how vaccination provides protection against disease. Discuss the role of modern **vaccination programmes** in preventing disease. Comment on the contribution of aggressive vaccination programmes to the eradication of some (named) infectious diseases. If required, outline the vaccination schedule for your country, identifying critical times for vaccination against specific diseases. Discuss the role of effective vaccination programmes in public health and the incidence of infectious disease.

☐ 12. Describe the principles involved in the production of vaccines. Giving examples, explain how vaccines are administered. Distinguish between **subunit** and **whole-agent vaccines** and between **inactivated** (dead) and **live** (attenuated) **vaccines**. Contrast the risks and benefits associated with live and dead vaccines.

☐ 13. Evaluate the risks associated with immunisation. Compare these risks with the risks associated with contracting the disease itself.

☐ 14. Describe and comment on the role of genetic engineering in the development of new vaccines.

Diagnosing Disease *(pages 85-90, 101-02, 111-12)*

☐ 15. Outline some of the technologies available for detecting and diagnosing diseases and homeostatic imbalances. Include any of: prenatal tests for inherited disorders (e.g. amniocentesis, CVS, ultrasound), postnatal tests, X-rays, CAT scans, MRI, biosensors.

☐ 16. Identify the role of the *Human Genome Project* in the further development of genetic screening programmes.

☐ 17. Explain what **monoclonal antibodies** are and explain how they are produced. Explain why they are so useful in medicine and outline some of their applications.

☐ 18. Describe the role of monoclonal antibodies in the diagnosis of disease. Recognise the application of monoclonal antibodies to the treatment of disease.

☐ 19. Outline the principles of **genetic counselling** and explain its role in the diagnosis of genetic disorders. Appreciate how this field has been expanded in the light of new technologies.

Treatment of Disease *(refer to pages listed below)*

Surgical treatments *(pages 39, 90, 117-120)*

☐ 20. Name some of the diseases that are most successfully treated with **surgery**. Using a named example, describe precisely how surgery is used to treat disease.

Therapeutic drugs *(pages 38-39, 95-98, 109-110)*

☐ 21. Discuss the use of **therapeutic drugs**, including **antimicrobial drugs** and **chemotherapy**, in treating disease. Outline the importance of new drug technologies in treating viral diseases such as HIV/AIDS. Describe the increasingly important role of recombinant DNA technologies in producing human proteins to treat disease.

☐ 22. Outline the ways in which drugs can work against:

(a) Bacterial diseases (see #24).
(b) Cancers (especially isolated tumours).
(c) Autoimmune diseases (e.g. rheumatoid arthritis).
(d) Allergic reactions (e.g. asthma).
(e) Viral diseases (e.g. AIDS, herpes, hepatitis B).

☐ 23. Outline the history of **antibiotic** discovery and use. Describe the importance of antibiotics to modern medicine, identifying the group of organisms against which they are (and are not) effective.

☐ 24. Explain how antibiotics work to prevent disease. Explain why particular antibiotics are effective against specific types of bacteria and not against others. Discuss the implications of **antibiotic resistance** to the continued, effective treatment of disease.

Radiotherapy *(pages 38-39)*

☐ 25. Discuss when and how radiation (**radiotherapy**) is used in the treatment of cancer. Outline the techniques and discuss the side effects associated with treatment.

Kidney dialysis *(page 123)*

☐ 26. Describe the technique and application of **kidney dialysis**. Explain how dialysis is used for restoring and maintaining homeostasis in cases of kidney failure.

Transplant technology *(pages 108, 117-122)*

☐ 27. Identify problems associated with the supply and transfusion of **blood** and blood products. Identify the need for an adequate blood substitute. Describe the problems associated with the production of **artificial blood**, outlining the reasons why blood is such a difficult product to produce by artificial means.

☐ 28. Describe the principles involved and the applications of **transplant technology**, including organ transplants. Outline the technical and ethical difficulties associated with the use of transplanted organs and tissues.

☐ 29. Describe the principles and techniques involved in **tissue engineering**. Discuss the benefits (including both the ethical and biological benefits) associated with the use of engineered tissues in medicine.

☐ 30. Explain what is meant by **stem cell technology**. Outline the properties of stem cells that make them potentially so useful in medicine and discuss their present and possible future applications.

Gene therapy *(pages 88, 111-116)*

☐ 31. Discuss the current and future role of **gene therapy** in treating disease. Explain the techniques involved in gene therapy and identify problems associated with these techniques and their application.

☐ 32. Identify the criteria that must be fulfilled in order for gene therapy to be feasible. Identify diseases that are potentially suitable for treatment with gene therapy.

☐ 33. Recognise the contribution of the **Human Genome Project** to the identification of diseases suitable for treatment by gene therapy methods.

See page 7 for additional details of this text:

■ Chenn, P. 1997. **Microorganisms and Biotechnology** (John Murray), chpt. 8 & 9 as reqd.

■ Freeland, P., 1999. **Microbes, Medicine and Commerce** (Hodder & Stoughton), chpt. 6.

■ Fullick, A., 1998. **Human Health and Disease** (Heinemann), chpt. 1 & 3 as required.

■ Hudson, T. & K. Mannion, 2001. **Microbes and Disease** (Collins), chpt .6.

■ Murray, P. & N. Owens, 2001. **Behaviour and Populations** (Collins), chpt. 7-8.

■ Taylor, J., 2001. **Microorganisms and Biotechnology** (NelsonThornes), chpt. 7.

See page 7 for details of publishers of periodicals:

STUDENT'S REFERENCE

■ **Rebuilding the Food Pyramid** Scientific American, January 2003, pp. 52-59. *A major revision of the basic nutritional guidelines. Critiques dietary information and gives an analysis of what we should be eating now (a good debate topic).*

■ **Antibiotics** Biol. Sci. Rev. May 1999, pp. 18-20. *Antibiotics: how they were discovered and how they work to kill their target organisms.*

■ **Finding and Improving Antibiotics** Biol. Sci. Rev. 12(1) Sept. 1999, pp. 36-38. *Antibiotics, their production & testing, and the search for new drugs.*

■ **MRSA, A Hosptial Superbug** Biol. Sci. Rev. 19(4) Apr. 2007. pp. 30-33. *The development of antibiotic resistance and the nature and significance of MRSA,*

■ **Genes, the Genome, and Disease** New Scientist, 17 Feb. 2001, (Inside Science). *Understanding the human genome: producing genome maps, the role of introns in gene regulation, and the future of genomic research.*

■ **Made to Measure Drugs** Biol. Sci. Rev., 14(4) April 2002, pp. 34-36. *The technical and ethical issues associated with the use of HGP information for the design of new drugs for individuals.*

■ **Genetic Screening - Controlling the Future** Biol. Sci. Rev., 12 (4) March 2000, pp. 36-38. *The techniques, applications, and ethical questions posed by genetic screening.*

■ **First Gene Therapy Approved** New Scientist, 29 November 2003, p. 13. *For the first time, a gene therapy based treatment has been given the go-ahead by regulatory authorities. The treatment consists of using an adenoviral vector to insert a p53 gene, coding for a protein that triggers cell suicide and attacks tumours.*

■ **A Dream Ticket for Tracking Disease** New Scientist 16 Jun. 2007, pp. 14-15. *Gene therapy using modified stem cells to treat human diseases.*

■ **Genes Can Come True** New Scientist, 30 Nov. 2002, pp. 30-33. *An overview of the current state of gene therapy, and a note about future directions.*

■ **What is a Stem Cell?** Biol. Sci. Rev., 16(2) November 2003, pp. 21-23. *An excellent account of the nature and uses of stem cell technology.*

■ **Tissue Engineering** Biol. Sci. Rev., 15(2) November 2002, pp. 17-19. *The technology and applications of growing tissue implants.*

■ **HIV Focus** New Scientist, 8 Feb. 2003, pp. 33-44. *A special issue covering HIV research, including vaccine development, and the new trend towards the use of protective microbiocides.*

■ **Genetic Vaccines** Scientific American, July 1999, pp. 34-41. *This excellent article includes a description of how the vaccines work and a table of specific diseases treatable by this method.*

■ **Defensive Eating** Scientific American, May. 2005, pp. 13-14. *Food vaccines developed as pills.*

■ **Preparing for Battle** Scientific American, Feb. 2001, pp. 68-69. *Preparation and mode of action of the influenza vaccine. Includes discussion of the problems associated with the changing virus.*

■ **The Power to Divide** National Geographic, 208(1) July 2005. *Examples where stem cell therapy or therapeutic cloning has worked remarkably well. Some of the ethical debates and funding issues in stem cell research are presented.*

TEACHER'S REFERENCE

■ **New Medicines for the Developing World** Biol. Sci. Rev. 14 (1) Sept. 2001, pp. 22-26. *The politics of treating disease in the developing world: why is there little incentive to develop programmes to prevent and treat some diseases?*

■ **The Search for Blood Substitutes** Scientific American, February 1998, pp. 60-65. *Blood substitutes could be the best way to prevent the transmission of infection during transfusion.*

■ **The Promise of Tissue Engineering** Scientific American, April 1999, pp. 37-65. *An excellent series of four articles examining the current techniques and applications of this new technology.*

■ **The Stem Cell Challenge** Scientific American, June 2004, pp. 60-67. *Many technical and ethical hurdles must be overcome before stem cell technology can be widely adopted. This account discusses both the techniques and possibilities.*

■ **The Business of the Human Genome** Scientific American, July 2000, pp. 38-57. *An account of the HGP: who is involved, how the information will be used, and where the research will progress from here.*

■ **Edible Vaccines** Scientific American, Sept. 2000, pp. 48-53. *Vaccines in food may be the way of future immunisation programmes.*

■ **Designing a Dilemma** New Scientist, 11 December 1999, pp. 18-19. *A short, but useful account of preimplantation and prenatal tests.*

See pages 4-5 for details of how to access **Bio Links** from our web site: **www.thebiozone.com** From Bio Links, access sites under the topics:

HEALTH & DISEASE: • CDC disease links • WHO/OMS: health topics > **Prevention and Treatment:** • Antibiotic resistance • Antimicrobial agents • How severe is antibiotic resistance? • Inducible defenses against pathogens • Monoclonal antibodies • Monoclonal antibody technology; the basics • Resistance to antibiotics

Also see the sites listed under the subtopics Infectious diseases and Non-infectious Diseases

Presentation MEDIA to support this topic:

HEALTH & DISEASE:
• **The Nature of Disease**
• **Non-Infectious Disease**

Health & Disease

Prenatal Diagnosis of Disease

Technological advances in recent decades have enabled greater control over conception, gestation, and birth. There are now a number of commonly used prenatal (before birth) diagnostic tests that can be used to investigate foetal health and development, and test for genetic abnormalities. Prenatal diagnoses vary a lot in terms of how invasive they are to the pregnancy and how much information they provide. Tests of the α-**fetoprotein** levels in the mother's blood serum can indicate **Down syndrome** (low α-fetoprotein) or **neural tube defects** (high α-fetoprotein) without

risk to the fetus. Other prenatal procedures (e.g. **ultrasound**) carry a low risk and have become almost routine in some societies. **Amniocentesis** and **chorionic villus sampling** present a greater risk to both the mother and fetus and are usually reserved for the detection of chromosomal abnormalities in high risk pregnancies. All prenatal diagnostic procedures should involve supportive and accurate counselling regarding the benefits and risks of the procedure, and the choices available should the pregnancy prove to be abnormal.

Related activities: The Fate of Conceptions, Genetic Counselling

RA 2

1. (a) Explain the medical reasons why an ultrasound scan might be used to examine a fetus:

_____

_____

(b) Name one other feature that may be detected with ultrasound: _____

(c) Explain why ultrasound scans are usually performed later in pregnancy (20 weeks):

_____

2. Chorionic villus sampling (CVS), if performed very early in pregnancy (at 5-7 weeks) may cause limb abnormalities, probably via upsetting critical sites of foetal blood flow. Suggest why CVS might be performed at such an early stage:

_____

3. Name one chromosomal disorder detectable through amniocentesis: _____

4. (a) Explain why amniocentesis is not usually recommended for women younger than 35:

_____

(b) Suggest when amniocentesis might be recommended for younger women, in spite of the risk:

_____

5. State two clinical indications for needing a prenatal test involving chromosome analysis:

(a) _____ (b) _____

6. Suggest why a history of infertility or miscarriage may indicate that a parent is carrying an inherited genetic disorder:

_____

7. Describe some of the ethical concerns of the following information gained through prenatal diagnoses:

(a) Gender determination: _____

_____

(b) Termination of a viable pregnancy: _____

_____

Postnatal Testing

There are a number of genetically inherited metabolic disorders in humans that involve interruption of metabolic pathways. Most are very rare with incidence rates of one in millions. However, some are common enough to warrant testing of all newborn babies (five days after birth). The baby's blood sample is taken by a nurse at the hospital, or a midwife or doctor at home, and blotted onto an absorbent card (see below). The sample is sent away for tests that could save the baby's life, or enable prevention of serious physical or mental problems. Most babies born in Britain are normal. A very few have rare, but serious disorders that are caused by a defective gene that gives rise to a defective protein. This protein is usually an enzyme that is unable to carry out its vital step in a metabolic pathway. Newborn blood tests are carried out at special testing centres in each country. In the UK (below), these laboratories currently test for three disorders, two of which are caused by recessive genes on autosomes.

1. Explain what is meant by a **metabolic disorder**: _____

_____

2. Explain briefly the purpose of the **newborn baby blood test**: _____

_____

3. Suggest why the blood samples are not taken until the 5th day after birth: _____

_____

4. Giving an example, define the term **congenital**: _____

_____

Related activities: Inherited Metabolic Disorders

RA 1

Genetic Counselling

Genetic counselling is an analysis of the risk of producing offspring with known gene defects within a family. Counsellors identify families at risk, investigate the problem present in the family, interpret information about the disorder, analyse inheritance patterns and risks of recurrence, and review available options with the family. Increasingly, there are DNA tests for the identification of specific defective genes. People usually consider genetic counselling if they have a family history of a genetic disorder, or if a routine prenatal screening test yields an unexpected result. While screening for many genetic disorders is now recommended, the use of presymptomatic tests for adult-onset disorders, such as Alzheimer's, is still controversial.

1. Outline the benefits of **carrier screening** to a couple with a family history of a genetic disorder:

   _____

   _____

2. (a) Suggest why Huntington disease persists in the human population when it is caused by a lethal, dominant allele:

   _____

   _____

   (b) Explain how presymptomatic genetic testing could change this: _____

   _____

   _____

Related activities: Inherited Metabolic Disorders, Prenatal Diagnosis
of Disease, The Human Genome Project

© BIOZONE International 2007
ISBN: 978-1-877462-13-9
Photocopying Prohibited

A 2

Diagnosing Medical Problems

The proper and prompt treatment of disease requires accurate and rapid diagnosis. Some diagnostic techniques, such as CT and MRI scans, are very sophisticated, while others (e.g. blood tests) are much less complicated. Examples are given below.

© BIOZONE International 2007
ISBN: 978-1-877462-13-9
Photocopying Prohibited

A 2

1. Describe the basic principle of the scanning technology behind each of the following computer imaging techniques:

   (a) Computerised Tomography (CT): _____

   _____

   (b) Magnetic Resonance Imaging (MRI): _____

   _____

2. Describe the benefits of using computer imaging techniques such as MRI or CT: _____

   _____

3. Explain how radionuclide scanning differs from X-rays: _____

   _____

4. Describe the benefits of endoscope technology over conventional open surgery: _____

   _____

5. Describe the basic principle of a biosensor: _____

   _____

   _____

   _____

© BIOZONE International 2007
ISBN: 978-1-877462-13-9
Photocopying Prohibited

A Balanced Diet

Nutrients are required for metabolism, tissue growth and repair, and as an energy source. Good nutrition (provided by a **balanced diet**) is recognised as a key factor in good health. Conversely poor nutrition (malnutrition) may cause ill-health or **deficiency diseases**. A diet refers to the quantity and nature of the food eaten. While not all foods contain all the representative nutrients, we can obtain the required balance of different nutrients by eating a wide variety of foods. In a recent overhaul of previous dietary recommendations, the health benefits of monounsaturated fats (such as olive and canola oils), fish oils, and whole grains have been recognised, and people are being urged to reduce their consumption of highly processed foods and saturated (rather than total) fat. Those on diets that restrict certain food groups (e.g. vegans) must take care to balance their intake of foods to ensure an adequate supply of protein and other nutrients (e.g. iron and B vitamins). **Reference Nutrient Intakes** (RNIs) in the UK (overleaf), and their equivalents in other countries, provide nutritional guidelines for different sectors of the population. They help to define the limits of adequate nutrient intake for most people, although not necessarily those with special needs.

1. Identify two major roles of **nutrients** in the diet:

   (a) _____

   (b) _____

2. (a) Compare the two food pyramids (above) and discuss how they differ in their recommendations for good nutrition:

   _____

   _____

   _____

   _____

   _____

   _____

   _____

   _____

Related activities: Deficiency Diseases, Dietary Disorders

DA 2

(b) Based on the information on the graph (right), state the evidence that might support the revised recommendations:

_____

_____

_____

_____

_____

_____

_____

3. With reference to the table above, contrast the nutritional requirements of non-pregnant and lactating women:

_____

_____

4. Suggest why recommendations (such as DRVs), which are based on the nutritional needs of most people in the population, might be preferable to those (such as RDAs) which try to encompass the needs of the whole population:

_____

_____

_____

5. Suggest how DRVs (or their equivalents) can be applied in each of the following situations:

(a) Dietary planning and assessment: _____

_____

(b) Food labelling and consumer information: _____

_____

The Health Benefits of Exercise

Regular exercise helps protect against a range of health problems, improves mood, and assists in managing stress. Exercise promotes health by improving the rate of blood flow back to the heart (**venous return**). This is achieved by strengthening all types of muscle and by increasing the efficiency of the heart. During exercise blood flow to different parts of the body changes in order to cope with the extra demands of the muscles, the heart and the lungs. Over time, regular exercise leads to greater **endurance**, and improves the body's ability to respond to everyday demands of physical activity.

1. (a) Explain how the body increases the rate of blood flow during exercise: _____

   _____

   (b) Describe the physiological effects of this when exercise is performed on a regular basis: _____

   _____

   (c) Explain how these changes benefit health in the long term: _____

   _____

   _____

   _____

2. The table (right) provides data for the **rate** of blood flow to various parts of the body at rest and during strenuous exercise. **Calculate** the **percentage** of the total blood flow that each organ or tissue receives under each regime of activity.

3. (a) State approximately how many times the total rate of blood flow increases between rest and exercise:

   _____

   (b) Explain why the increase is needed:

   _____

   _____

   _____

   _____

   _____

   _____

4. Identify the organs or tissues that show the most change in the rate of blood flow with exercise and explain why:

   _____

   _____

5. Suggest why heart size increases with cardiovascular endurance activity: _____

   _____

6. Heart stroke volume increases with endurance training. Explain how this increases the efficiency of the heart as a pump:

   _____

   _____

The Control of Disease

Many factors can influence the spread of disease, including the social climate, diet, general health, and access to medical care. Human intervention and modification of behaviour can reduce the transmission rate of some diseases and inhibit their spread. Examples include the use of personal physical barriers, such as condoms, to prevent sexually transmitted infections (STIs), and the use of **quarantine** to ensure that potential carriers of disease are isolated until incubation periods have elapsed. Cleaning up the environment also lowers the incidence of disease by reducing the likelihood that pathogens or their vectors will survive. The effective control of infectious disease depends on knowing the origin of the outbreak (its natural reservoir), its mode of transmission within the population, and the methods that can be feasibly employed to contain it. Diseases are often classified according to how they behave in a given population. Any disease that spreads from one host to another, either directly or indirectly, is said to be a **communicable disease**. Those that are easily spread from one person to another, such as chicken pox or measles, are said to be **contagious**. Such diseases are a threat to **public health** and many must be notified to health authorities. **Noncommunicable diseases** are not spread from one host to another and pose less of a threat to public health. A disease that occurs only occasionally and is usually restricted in its spread is called a **sporadic disease**.

1. Distinguish between contagious and non-communicable diseases, providing an example of each:

_____

_____

2. (a) Explain the difference between **isolation** and **quarantine**: _____

_____

_____

_____

Related activities: Patterns of Disease, HIV and AIDS

RA 2

(b) Using the example of SARS, explain how isolation and quarantine operate to prevent the spread of disease:

3. Explain how the use of condoms reduces the spread of the human immunodeficiency virus (HIV) that causes AIDS:

4. Explain how the drainage of stagnant water in tropical regions may reduce the incidence of malaria in those countries:

5. Describe how each of the following methods is used to control the **growth** of disease-causing microbes:

(a) Disinfectants:

(b) Antiseptics:

(c) Heat:

(d) Ionising radiation (gamma rays):

(e) Desiccation:

(f) Cold:

6. The **Human Genome Project** (HGP) has acheived its aim of sequencing the entire human genome, and much of the research since has focussed on determining the various roles of the (expressed) gene products. It is hoped that a more complete understanding the human genome will revolutionise the treatment and prevention of disease. Briefly discuss how the HGP will facilitate:

(a) Diagnosis of disease:

(b) Treatment of disease:

7. The first measles vaccine was introduced to Britain in 1964. However, in 1993 there were 9000 cases of measles notified to the health authorities in England and Wales.

(a) Suggest why measles has not been eliminated in Britain:

(b) Explain how vaccination interrupts the transmission of measles within a population:

Antimicrobial Drugs

Antimicrobial drugs include synthetic (manufactured) **drugs** as well as drugs produced by bacteria and fungi, called **antibiotics**. Antibiotics are produced naturally by these microorganisms as a means of inhibiting competing microbes around them (a form of antibiosis, hence the name antibiotic). The first antibiotic, called penicillin, was discovered in 1928 by Alexander Fleming. Since then, similar inhibitory reactions between colonies growing on solid media have been commonly observed. Antibiotics are actually rather easy to discover, but few of them are of medical or commercial value. Many antibiotics are toxic to humans or lack any advantage over those already in use. More than half of our antibiotics are produced by species of filamentous bacteria that commonly inhabit the soil, called **Streptomyces**. A few antibiotics are produced by bacteria of the genus **Bacillus**. Others are produced by moulds, mostly of the genera *Cephalosporium* and *Penicillium*. Antimicrobial drugs are used in **chemotherapy** programmes to treat infectious diseases. Like disinfectants, these chemicals interfere with the growth of microorganisms (see diagram below). They may either kill microbes directly (**bactericidal**) or prevent them from growing (**bacteriostatic**). To be effective, they must often act inside the host, so their effect on the host's cells and tissues is important. The ideal antimicrobial drug has **selective toxicity**, killing the pathogen without damaging the host. Some antimicrobial drugs have a narrow **spectrum of activity**, and affect only a limited number of microbial types. Others are **broad-spectrum drugs** and affect a large number of microbial species (see the table below). When the identity of a pathogen is not known, a broad-spectrum drug may be prescribed in order to save valuable time. There is a disadvantage with this, because broad spectrum drugs target not just the pathogen, but much of the host's normal microflora also. The normal microbial community usually controls the growth of pathogens and other microbes by competing with them. By selectively removing them with drugs, certain microbes in the community that do not normally cause problems, may flourish and become **opportunistic pathogens**.

Preventing & Treating Disease

Related activities: Resistance in Pathogens, Viral Diseases

A 2

1. Discuss the requirements of an "ideal" antimicrobial drug, and explain in what way antibiotics satisfy these requirements:

_____

_____

_____

_____

2. Some bacteria have ways of tolerating treatment by antibiotics, and are termed 'superbugs'.

   (a) Explain what is meant by **antibiotic resistance** in bacteria: _____

   _____

   _____

   (b) Explain why a course of antibiotics should be finished completely, even when the symptoms of infection have gone:

   _____

   _____

3. The spectrum of activity varies for different groups of drugs.

   (a) Explain the advantages and disadvantages of using a broad-spectrum drug on an unidentified bacterial infection:

   _____

   _____

   (b) Identify two broad spectrum groups of drugs: _____

4. Although there are a few drugs that have some success in controlling viruses, antibiotics are ineffective. Explain why antibiotics do not work against viruses:

_____

_____

5. Describe four ways in which antimicrobial drugs kill or inhibit the growth of microbes: _____

_____

_____

6. The diagram below shows an experiment investigating the effectiveness of different antibiotics on a pure culture of a single species of bacteria. Giving a reason, state which antibiotic (A-D) is most effective in controlling the bacteria:

_____

© BIOZONE International 2007
ISBN: 978-1-877462-13-9
Photocopying Prohibited

Resistance in Pathogens

Although many pathogens are controlled effectively with drugs and vaccines, the spread of drug resistance amongst microorganisms is increasingly undermining the ability to treat and control diseases such as tuberculosis and malaria. Methicillin resistant strains of the common bacterium *Staphylococcus aureus* (MRSA) have acquired genes that confer antibiotic resistance to all penicillins, including **methicillin** and other narrow-spectrum pencillin-type drugs. Such strains, called "superbugs", were discovered in the UK in 1961 and are now widespread, and the infections they cause are exceedingly difficult to treat. Genes for drug resistance arise through mutation, and the high mutation rates and short generation times of viral, bacterial, and protozoan pathogens have contributed to the rapid spread of drug resistance through populations. This is well documented for malaria, TB, and HIV/AIDS. Rapid evolution in pathogens is exacerbated too by the strong selection pressure created by the wide use and misuse of antimicrobial drugs, the poor quality of available drugs, and poor patient compliance. The most successful treatment for several diseases now appears to be a multi-pronged attack using a cocktail of drugs to target the pathogen at many stages.

Global Spread of Chloroquine Resistance

Areas of chloroquine resistance in *P. falciparum*.

Malaria in humans is caused by various species of *Plasmodium*, a protozoan parasite transmitted by *Anopheles* mosquitoes. The inexpensive antimalarial drug **chloroquine** was used successfully to treat malaria for many years, but its effectiveness has declined since resistance to the drug was first recorded in the 1960s. Chloroquine resistance has spread steadily (above) and now two of the four *Plasmodium* species, *P. falciparum* and *P. vivax* are chloroquine-resistant. *P. falciparum* alone accounts for 80% of all human malarial infections and 90% of the deaths, so this rise in resistance is of global concern. New anti-malarial drugs have been developed, but are expensive and often have undesirable side effects. Resistance to even these newer drugs is already evident, especially in *P. falciparum*, although this species is currently still susceptible to artemisinin, a derivative of the medicinal herb *Artemisia annua*.

Drug Resistance in HIV

Strains of drug-resistant HIV arise when the virus mutates during replication. Resistance may develop as a result of a single mutation, or through a step-wise accumulation of specific mutations. These mutations may alter drug binding capacity or increase viral fitness, or they may be naturally occurring polymorphisms (which occur in untreated patients). Drug resistance is likely to develop in patients who do not follow their treatment schedule closely, as the virus has an opportunity to adapt more readily to a "non-lethal" drug dose. The best practice for managing the HIV virus is to treat it with a cocktail of anti-retroviral drugs with different actions to minimise the number of viruses in the body. This minimises the replication rate, and also the chance of a drug resistant mutation being produced.

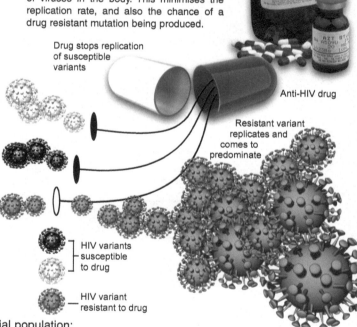

Drug stops replication of susceptible variants

Anti-HIV drug

Resistant variant replicates and comes to predominate

HIV variants susceptible to drug

HIV variant resistant to drug

1. Describe how genes for drug resistance arise in a microbial population:

_____

_____

2. Describe two mechanisms by which bacteria achieve drug resistance:

    (a) _____

    _____

    (b) _____

    _____

3. Explain how health authorities could target multiple drug resistance in common pathogens: _____

_____

_____

Methods by which Bacteria Acquire Resistance

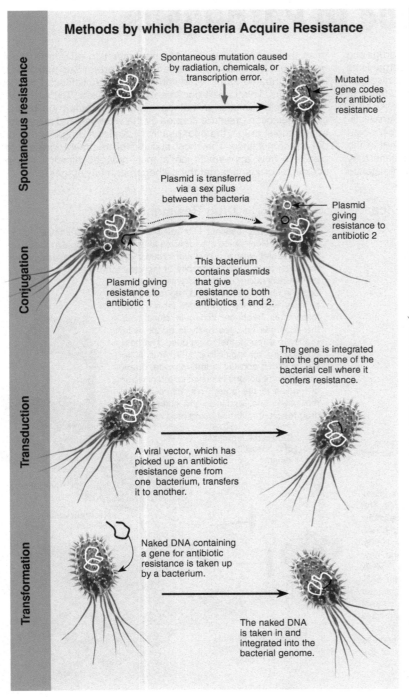

Spontaneous resistance

Spontaneous mutation caused by radiation, chemicals, or transcription error.

Mutated gene codes for antibiotic resistance

Conjugation

Plasmid is transferred via a sex pilus between the bacteria

Plasmid giving resistance to antibiotic 2

Plasmid giving resistance to antibiotic 1

This bacterium contains plasmids that give resistance to both antibiotics 1 and 2.

The gene is integrated into the genome of the bacterial cell where it confers resistance.

Transduction

A viral vector, which has picked up an antibiotic resistance gene from one bacterium, transfers it to another.

Transformation

Naked DNA containing a gene for antibiotic resistance is taken up by a bacterium.

The naked DNA is taken in and integrated into the bacterial genome.

Mechanisms of Resistance

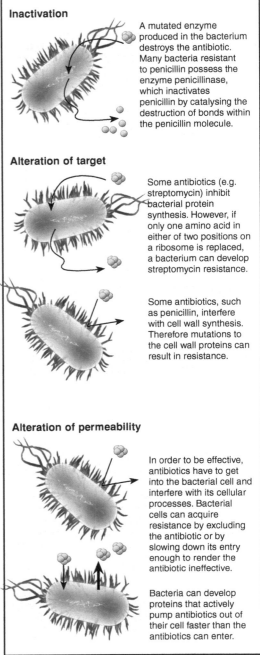

Inactivation

A mutated enzyme produced in the bacterium destroys the antibiotic. Many bacteria resistant to penicillin possess the enzyme penicillinase, which inactivates penicillin by catalysing the destruction of bonds within the penicillin molecule.

Alteration of target

Some antibiotics (e.g. streptomycin) inhibit bacterial protein synthesis. However, if only one amino acid in either of two positions on a ribosome is replaced, a bacterium can develop streptomycin resistance.

Some antibiotics, such as penicillin, interfere with cell wall synthesis. Therefore mutations to the cell wall proteins can result in resistance.

Alteration of permeability

In order to be effective, antibiotics have to get into the bacterial cell and interfere with its cellular processes. Bacterial cells can acquire resistance by excluding the antibiotic or by slowing down its entry enough to render the antibiotic ineffective.

Bacteria can develop proteins that actively pump antibiotics out of their cell faster than the antibiotics can enter.

4. Discuss the factors contributing to the rapid spread of drug resistance in pathogens: _____

_____

_____

_____

_____

_____

_____

_____

_____

_____

_____

_____

Monoclonal Antibodies

A **monoclonal antibody** is an artificially produced antibody that binds to and inactivates only one specific protein (antigen). Monoclonal antibodies are produced in the laboratory by stimulating the production of B-lymphocytes in mice injected with the antigen. These B-lymphocytes produce an antibody against the antigen. When isolated and made to fuse with immortal tumour cells, they can be cultured indefinitely in a suitable growing medium (as shown below). Monoclonal antibodies are useful for three reasons: they are totally uniform (i.e. clones), they can be produced in very large quantities at low cost, and they are highly specific. The uses of antibodies produced by this method range from diagnostic tools, to treatments for infections and cancer, and prevention of tissue rejection in transplant patients. Many of the diagnostic tests, e.g. for some sexually transmitted or parasitic infections, previously required relatively difficult culturing or microscopic methods for diagnosis. In addition, newer diagnostic tests using monoclonal antibodies are easier to interpret and often require fewer highly trained personnel.

Preventing & Treating Disease

1. Identify the mouse cells used to produce the monoclonal antibodies: _____

2. Describe the characteristic of tumour cells that allows an ongoing culture of antibody-producing lymphocytes to be made:

_____

_____

3. Compare the method of producing monoclonal antibodies using mice with the alternative methods now available:

_____

_____

_____

_____

Related activities: Antibodies

RA 2

102

4. For each of the following applications, suggest why an antibody-based test or therapy is so valuable:

(a) Detection of toxins or bacteria in perishable foods: _____

_____

_____

(b) Detection of pregnancy without a doctor's prescription: _____

_____

(c) Targeted treatment of tumours in cancer patients: _____

_____

Immunisation

A vaccine is a suspension of microorganisms (or pieces of them) that protects against disease by stimulating the production of antibodies and inducing **immunity**. **Vaccination** (often used synonymously with **immunisation**) is a procedure that provides **artificially acquired active immunity** in the recipient. A concerted vaccination campaign led to the eradication (in 1977) of **smallpox**, the only disease to have been eradicated in this way. Once eradicated, a pathogen is no longer present in the environment and vaccination is no longer necessary. Features of smallpox made it particularly suitable for complete eradication. It was a very recognisable and visible disease, with no long-term, human carriers and no non-human carriers. In addition, people who had not been vaccinated against the disease were identifiable by the absence of a vaccination scar on the upper arm. Disease control (as opposed to eradication) does not necessarily require that everyone be immune. **Herd immunity**, where most of the population is immune, limits outbreaks to sporadic cases because there are too few susceptible individuals to support an epidemic. Vaccination provides effective control over many common bacterial and viral diseases. Viral diseases in particular are best prevented with vaccination, as they cannot be effectively treated once contracted.

Related activities: Acquired Immunity, Types of Vaccine, Bacterial Diseases, Viral Diseases

RDA 2

1. The table below provides a list of the vaccines used in the standard vaccination schedule for children and young adults in the United Kingdom. Additional vaccinations are available for those at high risk of contracting certain diseases.

   (a) List the diseases that each vaccine protects against.

   (b) Determine the ages at which each vaccine should be administered. Place a tick (✔) in each age column as appropriate (the last one has been done for you). You can complete this for your own country if you wish. Schedules are available from www.thebiozone.com/vaccination.html and can be completed and used to replace the one shown.

2. The graph at the top of the previous page illustrates how a person reacts to the injection of the same antibody on two separate occasions. This represents the initial vaccination followed by a booster shot.

   (a) State over what time period the antigen levels were monitored: ⎯⎯⎯⎯⎯⎯⎯⎯⎯⎯⎯⎯⎯⎯⎯⎯⎯⎯

   (b) State what happens to the antibody levels after the first injection: ⎯⎯⎯⎯⎯⎯⎯⎯⎯⎯⎯⎯⎯⎯

   (c) State what happens to the antibody levels after the booster shot: ⎯⎯⎯⎯⎯⎯⎯⎯⎯⎯⎯⎯⎯⎯

   (d) Explain why the second injection has a markedly different effect: ⎯⎯⎯⎯⎯⎯⎯⎯⎯⎯⎯⎯⎯⎯

3. The whole question of whether young children should be immunised has been a point of hot debate with some parents. The parents that do not want their children immunised have strongly held reasons for doing so. In a balanced way, explore the arguments for and against childhood immunisation:

   (a) State clearly the benefits from childhood immunisation: ⎯⎯⎯⎯⎯⎯⎯⎯⎯⎯⎯⎯⎯⎯⎯⎯⎯⎯

   (b) Explain why some parents are concerned about immunising their children: ⎯⎯⎯⎯⎯⎯⎯⎯⎯⎯

4. Consult your family doctor or medical centre and list three vaccinations that are recommended for travellers to overseas destinations with high risk of infectious disease:

   (a) Country/region: ⎯⎯⎯⎯⎯⎯⎯ Vaccine required: ⎯⎯⎯⎯⎯⎯⎯

   (b) Country/region: ⎯⎯⎯⎯⎯⎯⎯ Vaccine required: ⎯⎯⎯⎯⎯⎯⎯

   (c) Country/region: ⎯⎯⎯⎯⎯⎯⎯ Vaccine required: ⎯⎯⎯⎯⎯⎯⎯

© BIOZONE International 2007
ISBN: 978-1-877462-13-9
Photocopying Prohibited

There are two basic types of vaccine: subunit vaccines and whole-agent vaccines. **Whole-agent vaccines** contain complete nonvirulent microbes, either **inactivated** (killed), or alive but **attenuated** (weakened). Attenuated viruses make very effective vaccines and often provide life-long immunity without the need for booster immunisations. Killed viruses are less effective, and many vaccines of this sort have now been replaced by newer subunit vaccines. **Subunit vaccines** contain only the parts of the pathogen that induce the immune response. They are safer than attenuated vaccines because they cannot reproduce in the recipient, and they produce fewer adverse effects because they contain little or no extra material. Subunit vaccines can be made using a variety of methods, including cell fragmentation (*acellular vaccines*), inactivation of toxins (*toxoids*), genetic engineering (*recombinant vaccines*), and combination with antigenic proteins (*conjugated vaccines*). In all cases, the subunit vaccine loses its ability to cause disease but retains its antigenic properties so that it is still effective in inducing an immune response. Some of the most promising types of vaccine under development are the **DNA vaccines**, consisting of naked DNA (encoding the antigen) which is injected into the body and produces an antigenic protein. So far, no experimental trials have provoked an immunological response strong enough to protect against disease, and their usefulness remains unproven.

Related activities: Immunisation, Edible Vaccines

RA 3

1. Describe briefly **how** each of the following types of vaccine are made and name an **example** of each:

   (a) Whole-agent vaccine: _____

   _____

   (b) Subunit vaccine: _____

   _____

   (c) Inactivated vaccine: _____

   _____

   (d) Attenuated vaccine: _____

   _____

   (e) Recombinant vaccine: _____

   _____

   (f) Toxoid vaccine: _____

   _____

   (g) Conjugated vaccine: _____

   _____

   (h) Acellular vaccine: _____

   _____

2. **Attenuated viruses** provide long term immunity to their recipients and generally do not require booster shots. Suggest a possible reason why attenuated viruses provide such effective long-term immunity when inactivated viruses do not:

   _____

   _____

3. Bearing in mind the structure of viruses, explain why **heat** cannot be used to kill viruses to make **inactivated vaccines**:

   _____

   _____

4. (a) Vaccines may now be produced using **recombinant DNA technology**. Describe an advantage of creating vaccines using these methods:

   _____

   (b) Draw a simple diagram to illustrate the use of the recombinant method to manufacture a vaccine:

Edible Vaccines

Although still a few years away, the development of edible vaccines produced by transgenic plants will overcome many of the problems faced when using traditional, injectable vaccines. Plants engineered to contain the vaccine can be grown locally, in the area where vaccination is required, overcoming the logistic and economic problems of transporting prepared vaccines over long distances. Most importantly, edible vaccines do not require syringes, saving money and eliminating the risk of infection from contaminated needles. One method used to generate edible vaccines relies on the bacterium *Agrobacterium tumefaciens* to deliver the genes for viral or bacterial antigens into plant cells. The diagram below illustrates this process using potatoes.

1. DESCRIBE two **advantages** of using edible vaccines:

   (a) _____

   (b) _____

2. Outline one **disadvantage** of using edible vaccines: _____

3. Although potatoes are easy to propagate and are grown in many regions of the world, they are not particularly suitable for use as edible vaccines because cooking denatures the antigenic proteins. Giving a reason, suggest another fruit or vegetable that would be more suitable:

   _____

   _____

4. Explain why a gene for antibiotic resistance is added to the bacterium: _____

   _____

Related activities: Immunisation, Types of Vaccines

A 2

The Search for Blood Substitutes

Blood's essential homeostatic role is evident when considering the problems encountered when large volumes of blood are lost. Transfusion of whole blood (see photograph below) or plasma is an essential part of many medical procedures, e.g. after trauma or surgery, or as a regular part of the treatment for some disorders (e.g. thalassaemia). This makes blood a valuable commodity. A blood supply relies on blood donations, but as the demand for blood increases, the availability of donors continues to decline. This decline is partly due to more stringent screening of donors for diseases such as HIV/AIDS, hepatitis, and variant CJD. The inadequacy of blood supplies has made the search for a safe, effective blood substitute the focus of much research. Despite some possibilities, no currently available substitute reproduces all of blood's many homeostatic functions.

1. Describe two essential features of a successful blood substitute, identifying briefly why the feature is important:

   (a) _____

   (b) _____

2. Name the two classes of artificial blood substitutes: _____

3. Discuss the advantages and risks associated with the use of blood substitutes: _____

   _____

   _____

   _____

   _____

   _____

A 2   **Related activities**: The Homeostatic Role of Blood

© BIOZONE International 2007
ISBN: 978-1-877462-13-9
Photocopying Prohibited

Production of Human Proteins

Transgenic microorganisms are now widely used as **biofactories** for the production of human proteins. These proteins are often used to treat metabolic protein-deficiency disorders. **Type 1 diabetes mellitus** is a metabolic disease caused by a lack of insulin and is treatable only with insulin injection. Before the advent of genetic engineering, insulin was extracted from the pancreatic tissue of pigs or cattle. This method was expensive and problematic in that the insulin caused various side effects and was often contaminated. Since the 1980s, human insulin has been mass produced using genetically modified (GM) bacteria (*Escherichia coli*) and yeast (*Saccharomyces cerevisiae*). Similar methods are used for the genetic manipulation of both microorganisms, although the size of the bacterial plasmid requires that the human gene be inserted as two, separately expressed, nucleotide sequences (see below). The use of insulin from GM sources has greatly improved the management of Type 1 diabetes, and the range of formulations now available has allowed diabetics to live much more normal lives than previously.

Related activities: Type 1 Diabetes, Gene Therapy

A 3

1. Describe the three major problems associated with the traditional method of obtaining insulin to treat diabetes:

(a) _____

(b) _____

(c) _____

2. Explain why the insulin gene is synthesized as two separate A and B chain nucleotide sequences: _____

_____

3. Explain why the synthetic nucleotide sequences ('genes') are inserted into the β-galactosidase gene: _____

_____

4. Yeast (*Saccharomyces cerevisiae*) is also used in the production of human insulin. It is a eukaryote with a larger plasmid than *E. coli*. Its secretory pathways are more similar to those of humans and β-galactosidase is not involved in gene expression. Predict how these differences might change the procedure for insulin production with respect to:

(a) Insertion of the gene into the plasmid: _____

_____

(b) Secretion and purification of the protein product: _____

_____

5. Describe the benefits to patients of using GMOs to produce human proteins: _____

_____

_____

6. When delivered to a patient, artificially produced human proteins only alleviate disease symptoms; they cannot cure the disease. Describe how this situation might change in the future:

_____

_____

_____

The **Human Genome Project** (HGP) was a publicly funded venture involving many different organisations throughout the world. In 1998, Celera Genomics in the USA began a competing project, as a commercial venture, in a race to be the first to determine the human genome sequence. In 2000, both organisations reached the first draft stage, and the entire genome is now available as a high quality (golden standard) sequence. In addition to determining the order of bases in the human genome, genes are being identified, sequenced, and mapped (their specific chromosomal location identified). Other challenges include assigning functions to the identified genes. By identifying and studying the protein products of genes (a field known as **proteomics**), scientists can develop a better understanding of genetic disorders. Long term benefits of the HGP are both medical and non-medical (overleaf). Many biotechnology companies have taken out patents on gene sequences. This practice is controversial because it restricts the use of the sequence information to the patent holders. Other genome sequencing projects have arisen as a result of the initiative to sequence the human one. A somewhat controversial project to map the differences between racial and ethnic groups is the **Human Genome Diversity Project** (HGDP). It aims to understand the degree of diversity amongst individuals in the human species.

Related activities: Genetic Counselling

RA 2

1. Briefly describe the objectives of the Human Genome Project (HGP) and the Human Genome Diversity Project (HGDP):

   HGP: _____

   _____

   HGDP: _____

2. Suggest a reason why indigenous peoples around the world are reluctant to provide DNA samples for the HGDP:

   _____

   _____

3. Describe two possible **benefits** of Human Genome Project (HGP):

   (a) Medical: _____

   _____

   (b) Non-medical: _____

   _____

4. Explain what is meant by **proteomics** and explain its significance to the HGP and the ongoing benefits arising from it:

   _____

   _____

   _____

   _____

5. Suggest two possible points of view for one of the **ethical issues** described in the list above:

   (a) _____

   _____

   (b) _____

   _____

Gene Therapy

Gene therapy refers to the application of gene technology to correct or replace defective genes. It was first envisioned as a treatment, or even a cure, for genetic disorders, but it could also be used to treat a wide range of diseases, including those that resist conventional treatments. Gene therapy may operate by providing a correctly working version of a faulty gene or by adding a **novel gene** to perform a corrective role. In other cases, gene expression may be blocked in order to control cellular (or viral) activity. About two thirds of currently approved gene therapy procedures are targeting cancer, about one quarter aim to treat genetic disorders, such as cystic fibrosis, and the remainder are attempting to provide relief for infectious diseases. Gene therapy requires a **gene delivery system**; a way to transfer the gene to the patient's cells. This may be achieved using a infectious agent such as a virus; a technique called **transfection**. A promising development has been the recent approval for gene therapy to be used in treating tumours in cancer patients. Severe combined immune deficiency syndrome (SCIDS) has also shown improvement after gene therapy. Infants treated for this inherited, normally lethal condition have become healthy young adults (see below). Gene therapy involving **somatic cells** may be therapeutic, but the genetic changes are not inherited. The transfection of **stem cells**, rather than mature somatic cells, achieves a longer persistence of therapy in patients. In the future, the introduction of corrective genes into **germline cells** will enable genetic corrections to be inherited.

1. (a) Describe the general purpose of gene therapy: _____

(b) Identify three general categories of disease currently targeted by gene therapy: _____

2. (a) Explain what is meant by **transfection**: _____

(b) Explain the significance of transfecting **germline cells** rather than **somatic** (body) cells: _____

3. Describe the purpose of **gene cloning** in gene therapy: _____

4. Suggest why **enzyme disorders** are good candidates for treatment using gene therapy: _____

Related activities: Vectors for Gene Therapy, Gene Delivery Systems

RA 2

Vectors for Gene Therapy

Gene therapy usually requires a **vector** (carrier) to introduce the DNA. The majority of approved clinical gene therapy protocols (63%) employ **retroviral vectors** to deliver the selected gene to the target cells, although there is considerable risk in using these vectors (below). Other widely used vectors include adenoviral vectors (16%), and liposomes (13%). The remaining 8% employ a variety of vector systems, the majority of which include injection of naked plasmid DNA.

1. (a) Describe the features of viruses that make them well suited as **vectors** for gene therapy: _____

_____

_____

   (b) Identify two problems with using viral vectors for gene therapy: _____

_____

_____

2. (a) Suggest why it may be beneficial for a (therapeutic) gene to integrate into the patient's chromosome:

_____

_____

   (b) Explain why this has the potential to cause problems for the patient: _____

_____

3. (a) Suggest why naked DNA is likely to be unstable within a patient's tissues: _____

_____

   (b) Suggest why enclosing the DNA within liposomes might provide greater stability: _____

_____

© BIOZONE International 2007
ISBN: 978-1-877462-13-9
Photocopying Prohibited

Related activities: Gene Therapy, Gene Delivery Systems

Gene Delivery Systems

The mapping of the human genome has improved the feasibility of gene therapy as a option for treating an increasingly wide range of diseases, but it remains technically difficult to deliver genes successfully to a patient. Even after a gene has been identified, cloned, and transferred to a patient, it must be expressed normally. To date, the success of gene therapy has been generally poor, and improvements have been short-lived or counteracted by adverse side effects. Inserted genes may reach only about 1% of target cells and those that reach their destination may work inefficiently and produce too little protein, too slowly to be of benefit. In addition, many patients react immunologically to the vectors used in gene transfer. Much of the current research is focussed on improving the efficiency of gene transfer and expression. One of the first gene therapy trials was for **cystic fibrosis** (CF). CF was an obvious candidate for gene therapy because, in most cases, the disease is caused by a single, known gene mutation. However, despite its early promise, gene therapy for this disease has been disappointing (below).

1. A great deal of current research is being devoted to discovering a gene therapy solution to treat **cystic fibrosis** (CF):

   (a) Describe the symptoms of CF: _____

   _____

   _____

   (b) Explain why this genetic disease has been so eagerly targeted by gene therapy researchers: _____

   _____

   _____

   _____

   _____

   (c) Outline some of the problems so far encountered with gene therapy for CF: _____

   _____

   _____

   _____

   _____

   _____

2. Identify two vectors for introducing healthy CFTR genes into CF patients. For each vector, outline how it might be delivered to the patient and describe potential problems with its use:

   (a) Vector 1: _____

   Delivery: _____

   Problems: _____

   _____

   _____

   (b) Vector 2: _____

   Delivery: _____

   Problems: _____

   _____

   _____

3. Changes made to chromosomes as a result of gene therapy involving somatic cells are not inherited. Germ-line gene therapy has the potential to cure disease, but the risks and benefits are still not clear. For each of the points outlined below, evaluate the risk of germ-line gene therapy relative to somatic cell gene therapy and explain your answer:

   (a) Chance of interfering with an essential gene function: _____

   _____

   _____

   _____

   (b) Misuse of the therapy to selectively alter phenotype: _____

   _____

   _____

   _____

Correcting Heart Problems

Over the last decade the death rates from CVD have slowly declined, despite an increase in its prevalence. This reduction in mortality has been achieved partly through better management and treatment of the disease. Medical technology now provides the means to correct many heart problems, even if only temporarily. Some symptoms of CVD, arising as a result of blockages to the coronary arteries, are now commonly treated using techniques such as coronary bypass surgery and angioplasty. Other cardiac disorders, such as disorders of heartbeat, are frequently treated using cardiac pacemakers. Valve defects, which are often congenital, can be successfully corrected with surgical valve replacement. The latest technology, still in its trial phase, involves non-surgical replacement of aortic valves. The procedure, known as percutaneous (through the skin) heart valve replacement, will greatly reduce the trauma associated with correcting these particular heart disorders.

1. Explain why patients who have undergone coronary bypass surgery or angioplasty require careful supervision of their diet and lifestyle following the operation, even though their problem has been alleviated:

   _____

   _____

2. (a) State the type of valve that would be used for an elderly patient needing a valve replacement: _____

   (b) Explain the reasons for your answer: _____

   _____

3. Explain the problems associated with the use of each type of replacement valve:

   (a) Tissue valves: _____

   (b) Synthetic valves: _____

Related activities: Diagnosing Medical Problems, Cardiovascular Disease

RA 2

4. Describe two techniques used to diagnose heart problems:

(a) _____

_____

(b) _____

_____

5. Describe two modern techniques for treatment of the effects of atherosclerosis in the coronary arteries:

(a) _____

_____

_____

(b) _____

_____

_____

6. Explain why it is necessary for the heart to receive regular electrical stimulation: _____

_____

_____

7. (a) Describe the purpose of a cardiac pacemaker, explaining how it achieves its effect: _____

_____

(b) Explain why a temporary pacemaker is often useful for a short time after cardiac surgery: _____

_____

_____

Organ Transplants

Transplant surgery involves the replacement of a diseased tissue or organ with a healthy, living substitute. The tissue or organ is usually taken from a person who has just died, although some (e.g. blood, kidneys, bone marrow) can be taken from living donors. Around the world, more than 100 000 major organs have been transplanted, mostly in the past few decades. About 80% of patients are alive and well one year after the transplantation, and most survive at least 5 years. There is always a great shortage of donors for organ transplants. Recently, there has been much concern over an emerging black market in body organs and tissue. Attempts to carry out transplants of organs from other species into humans (**xenotransplantation**) have not been very successful due to rejection, although there are hopes that **genetically modified** pigs may be used to produce organs especially altered to overcome immune rejection in human recipients. The success of organ transplants today has been the result of more effective **immunosuppressant drugs**, improved **tissue-typing**, and better techniques for organ preservation and transport. With the advent of **tissue engineering** and stem cell technology, researchers are rapidly moving towards creating semisynthetic, living organs that may be used as human replacement parts. Artificial skin has already been successfully developed, and more complex organs, such as the liver, may be possible using the same technology within 20 years.

Preventing & Treating Disease

Related activities: The Search for Blood Substitutes, Stem Cells and Tissue Engineering

A 2

1. Describe three major technical advances that have improved the success rate of organ transplantation:

(a) _____

(b) _____

(c) _____

2. (a) Explain the basis for organ and tissue rejection: _____

_____

_____

(b) Discuss the role of **tissue typing** and **immunosuppressant drugs** in reducing or preventing this response:

_____

_____

_____

(c) Describe one of the major undesirable side-effects of using immunosuppressant drugs in transplant recipients:

_____

3. Briefly describe the following technologies that are being developed in response to the shortage of donor organs:

(a) Xenotransplantation: _____

_____

(b) Tissue engineering: _____

_____

4. In point form, outline the ethical issues associated with organ and tissue transplants. Consider costs, benefits, source of tissue, and criteria for choosing recipients. If required, debate the issue, or develop your arguments as a separate report:

_____

_____

_____

_____

_____

_____

_____

© BIOZONE International 2007
ISBN: 978-1-877462-13-9
Photocopying Prohibited

Stem Cells and Tissue Engineering

Cell cultures have been used for many years for medical and research purposes, e.g. for the culture of viruses for vaccine production and in the production of monoclonal antibodies. Reliable techniques in cell culturing have paved the way for new technologies such as **cell replacement therapy** and **tissue engineering**. These technologies require a disease-free and plentiful supply of cells of specific types. Tissue engineering, for example, involves inducing living cells to grow on a scaffold of natural or synthetic material to produce a three-dimensional tissue such as bone or skin. In 1998, an artificial skin called Apligraf became the first product of this type to be approved for use as a biomedical device. It is now widely used in place of skin grafts. The applications of tissue engineering range from blood vessel replacement and skin, bone, tendon, and cartilage repair, to the treatment of degenerative nerve diseases. A key to the future of this technology will be the developments in **stem cell** research. Stem cells have the ability to develop and form all the tissues of the body. The best source of these is from very early embryos, but some adult tissues (e.g. bone marrow) also contain stem cells. Therapeutic **stem cell cloning** is still in its very early stages and, despite its enormous medical potential, research with human embryonic cells is still banned in some countries.

Preventing & Treating Disease

Related activities: Gene Therapy, Type 1 Diabetes

RA 3

1. Outline the benefits of using an tissue engineered skin product, such as Apligraf, to treat wounds that require grafts:

_____

_____

2. Describe one potential advantage of embryonic stem cell cloning for tissue engineering technology:

_____

_____

3. Discuss the present and potential medical applications of tissue engineering: _____

_____

_____

_____

_____

4. Investigate the techniques or the applications of therapeutic stem cell cloning and prepare a short account discussing the technical or ethical issues involved.

_____

_____

_____

_____

_____

_____

_____

_____

_____

_____

_____

_____

_____

_____

_____

_____

_____

_____

_____

_____

_____

Kidney Dialysis

A dialysis machine is a machine designed to remove wastes from the blood. It is used when the kidneys fail, or when blood acidity, urea, or potassium levels increase much above normal. In kidney dialysis, blood flows through a system of tubes composed of semi-permeable membranes. Dialysis fluid (**dialysate**) has a composition similar to blood except that the concentration of wastes is low. It flows in the opposite direction to the blood on the outside of the dialysis tubes. Consequently, waste products like urea diffuse from the blood into the dialysis fluid, which is constantly replaced. The dialysis fluid flows at a rate of several 100 cm^3 per minute over a large surface area. For some people dialysis is an ongoing procedure, but for others dialysis just allows the kidneys to rest and recover.

Preventing & Treating Disease

1. In kidney dialysis, explain why the dialysing solution is constantly replaced rather than being recirculated:

_____

_____

2. Explain why ions such as potassium and sodium, and small molecules such as glucose, do not diffuse rapidly from the blood into the dialysing solution along with the urea:

_____

_____

3. Explain why the urea passes from the blood into the dialysing solution: _____

_____

4. Describe the general transport process involved in dialysis: _____

_____

5. Give a reason why the dialysing solution flows in the opposite direction to the blood: _____

_____

_____

6. Explain why a clot and bubble trap is needed after the blood has been dialysed but before it re-enters the body:

_____

_____

_____

ISBN: 978-1-877462-13-9

A 2

Index